Scalpels & Buggywhips

Scalpels & Buggywhips

Medical Pioneers of Central BC

Eldon Lee

Copyright © 1997 Eldon Lee

CANADIAN CATALOGUING IN PUBLICATION DATA

Lee, Eldon, 1923-
Scalpels and buggywhips

ISBN 1-895811-43-0

1.   Physicians—British Columbia—Biography
2.   Frontier and pioneer life—British Columbia
I.   Title

R464.A1L43 1997   610'.92'711   C97-910627-3

First Edition 1997

Heritage House wishes to acknowledge the support of Heritage Canada, the British Columbia Arts Council and the BC Archives and Records Service (BCARS) for their support.

Cover Design: Darlene Nickull
Layout: Darlene Nickull and Catherine Mack
Edited by: Joanne Richardson
Cover Photo: Mural of Dr. Gerald (Paddy) Baker, Quesnel's G.R. Baker Memorial Hospital. Courtesy of Branwen Patenaude, painted by Peter Hopkinson, June 1956.

HERITAGE HOUSE PUBLISHING COMPANY LTD.
Unit #8 - 17921 55th Ave., Surrey, BC V3S 6C4

Printed in Canada

Contents

Chapter 2 written by Dr. Al Holley
Chapter 9 written by Dr. J.G. McKenzie and Dr. Eldon Lee
Chapter 16 written by Dr. J.G. McKenzie and Dr. Eldon Lee
Chapter 17 written by Dr. J.G. McKenzie

Hippocratic Oath

I swear by Apollo, the physician, and Asclepius and Health and All-Heal and all the gods and goddesses that, according to my ability and judgement, I will keep this oath and stipulation:

To reckon him who taught me this art equally dear to me as my parents, to share my substance with him and relieve his necessities if required; to regard his offspring as on the same footing with my own brothers, and to teach them this art if they should wish to learn it, without fee or stipulation, and that by precept, lecture and every other mode of instruction, I will impart a knowledge of the art to my own sons and to those of my teachers, and to disciples bound by a stipulation and oath, according to the law of medicine, but to none others.

I will follow that method of treatment which, according to my ability and judgment, I consider for the benefit of my patients, and abstain from whatever is deleterious and mischievous. I will give no deadly medicine to anyone if asked, nor suggest any such counsel; furthermore, I will not give to a woman an instrument to produce abortion.

With purity and with holiness I will pass my life and practise my art. I will not cut a person who is suffering from a stone, but will leave this to be done by practitioners of this work. Into whatever houses I enter I will go into them for the benefit of the sick and will abstain from every voluntary act of mischief and corruption; and further from the seduction of females or males, bond or free.

Whatever, in connection with my professional practice, or not in connection with it, I may see or hear in the lives of men which ought not to be spoken abroad I will not divulge, as reckoning that all such should be kept secret.

While I continue to keep this oath inviolated may it be granted to me to enjoy life and the practice of the art, respected by all men at all times but should I trespass and violate this oath, may the reverse be my lot.

Hippocrates of Kos 460–400 BC
Father of Western Medicine

This sturdy two-seat surrey, a matched pair of sound work horses, and a standard buggywhip typify a pioneer doctor's traditional mode of transport. This photo was taken in the Cariboo at 141 Mile House in the 1890s.
(BCARS)

FOREWORD

The Medical Pioneers

The forces that brought pioneer healers to central British Columbia were many and varied: for the early Native tribes and their shamans it was the possibility of a better life, a plentiful food supply, and a land of their own; for the early White medical pioneers it was the lure of gold, religious fervour, the opportunity to fill a medical need, or simply a sense of adventure. All of these people were endowed with that extra dimension of human vitality—a daring spirit.

This spirit led them to test a new frontier and to try their endurance and toughness against many trials and hardships. Nothing daunted them; they treated everything from scurvy to grizzly-bear bites, delivered babies, and performed surgery that would tax the resources of skilled surgeons in major hospitals.

In a book such as this, it is difficult to set time and geographical limits. I have been very liberal in setting 10,000 years ago as the date when Native shamans came across from Siberia and the year 1920 as the date after which most of the Interior hospitals were present in one form or another. For geographical boundaries I have chosen Clinton to the south, Prince George to the north, Hazelton and Anahim Lake to the west, and McBride to the east. This vast territory is gripped by a harsh winter five months of the year and variable weather for the other seven. This land is plagued by insects and difficult terrain, and it is to the hardy medical pioneers who practised within its boundaries that this book is dedicated.

In writing this book I have tried to get as close to the subjects as possible. I knew Dr Lyon and Dr Baker personally, and others I have come to know through interviews with relatives, friends, and former patients. All were human and part of life's stream—even as they seemed to stand above the flood. Their personalities, intellects, manners of practice, and reaction to crushing responsibilities lifted them to greatness in spite of their human frailties.

Dr Al Holley, a Fellowship Specialist in Surgery, who writes of the medical doctors of Barkerville, grew up in Quesnel and maintains a keen interest in western historical events. He has played the part of Dr Thomas Bell in Barkerville theatrical productions.

Dr Jack McKenzie, born and raised in Prince George, graduated from the University of Manitoba. He had a family practice in Prince George and knew Father Coccola, Dr Eddie Lyon, and Dr Carl Ewert.

A past president of the College of Physicians and Surgeons of British Columbia, he has been honoured by Her Majesty, Queen Elizabeth II, and by His Holiness, Pope John Paul.

I suppose that I started collecting material for this book when, as a boy of five, I moved with my family from California to the Williams Lake area. The intervening years have, for the most part, been spent in central British Columbia. I began more intensive work on the book in 1967, when I interviewed Molly Forbes, a pioneer of Clinton and Lac la Hache. At this time I was swamped with work, as I was the only consulting specialist in the field of obstetrics and gynaecology in the central Interior. I recorded a dozen interviews and put them aside for 25 years. I now appreciate having begun compiling information at an early date, as sources have gradually dwindled due to the ravages of time and natural attrition.

In many ways the recollections of the pioneer settlers are the most valid sources of information, as their anecdotes provide a means of appreciating the various personalities of these early medical people.

Jessie Gould of Hazelton, now 86 years old, accompanied her mother aboard the first Grand Trunk Pacific train from Prince Rupert to New Hazelton in 1912. She knew Dr Wrinch as a friend and as her own family doctor. She supplied volumes of handwritten historical records and many pictures of the Hazelton area. In addition she supplied copies of the letters of Robert Tomlinson Jr, the son of Dr Tomlinson.

Alice Keefe and the late Jean McKenna, pioneers of Francois Lake and Burns Lake, provided details of early medicine in that area. Marion Mummary, the first White child born in the Prosser Point Hospital at Francois Lake, recounted further incidents and anecdotes.

I am grateful to Grace Foote, Roy Foote, Millie Hendrie, and Vesta Philpott of Fort Fraser and the Fraser Lake area. They provided much useful information on Dr Lazier, Dr Cuzner, and railway construction camp doctors.

The late Ted Williams and the late Gladys Boehler of Prince George were invaluable sources of information for the Prince George area, as were Lil McIntosh, Margaret Calvert, and Dr Al Mooney for the Vanderhoof area.

Gertrude Watt Fraser (former matron of the Quesnel Hospital and niece of Dr Hugh Watt of Barkerville), Maude Lebourdais, Dr Al Holley, and Alice Lindstom provided colourful and enlightening insights into the complex character of Dr G.R. Baker.

Molly Forbes, the late Laura Moxan, Irene Stangoe, Veera Bonner, Irene Bliss, Hazel Litterick, June Bliss, Bonnie Church, Dr John Roberts, and the late Pat Mayfield provided information on Dr Wright of Alexis Creek, the 150 Mile House doctors, and Dr George Sanson of Clinton.

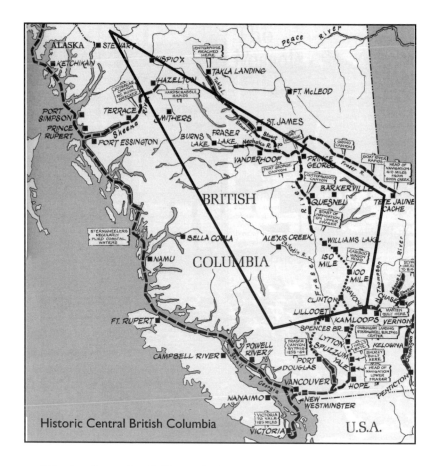

Historic Central British Columbia

My thanks to the College of Physicians and Surgeons of British Columbia and Adrienne Clark of the College Library Service for details on the registration and training of early doctors. Thanks also to the Burns Lake, Fraser Lake, and Vanderhoof historical societies; the British Columbia Archives and Records Service (BCARS) in Victoria; and the Fraser Fort George, Quesnel, Barkerville, and Clinton museums. All provided pictures and information.

Finally, I wish to express gratitude to Dr Jack McKenzie and Dr Al Holley for their contribution to this book, both with regard to writing chapters and to providing encouragement and helpful information.

Eldon Lee, MD, FRCS(C), 1997

This Carrier Shaman, Houston Tommy, lived
near Hazelton.
Courtesy of Jessie Gould.

The local medicine man, this Hazelton
area shaman poses for the camera in
1914. (BCARS A-06041)

CHAPTER I

Shamans

For thousands of years Native shamans filled the role of healers in central British Columbia. Tribes came over the land bridge from Siberia around 10,000 years ago, and each tribe or village seemed to have a shaman. In spite of their skills, life was exceedingly short and brutish for these migrants into a forbidding territory. However, the plentiful salmon runs and abundant game of the New World proved to be a powerful attraction, and tribe after tribe migrated across the land bridge. Each succeeding wave either passed through the lands where a tribe was already established or, if powerful enough, dislodged the inhabitants. Some tribes shuttled through to the southwestern United States, and others moved eastward into Alberta, through northern Canada, and into Ontario.

Historically, according to Fraser Symington (1969), seven distinct aboriginal language groups were identified in British Columbia: the Tsimshian, the Athapaskan, the Haida, the Tagish, the Salish, the Nootka/Kwakiutl, and the Kootaney. (Modern anthropologists now recognize ten ethnic divisions in British Columbia: the Haida, the Tsimshian, the Kwakwaka'wakw, the Nuu Chah Nulth, the Nuxalk, the Coast Salish, the Interior Salish, the Kootaney, the Athapaskan (which includes the Chilcotin, Carrier, Sekani, Tahltan, Kaska, Slave, Beaver, Tsetsaut, and Nicola), and the Inland Tlingit. Of these, three are found in central British Columbia: the Tsimshian in the Hazelton-Kispiox area, the Carrier from Hazelton east to the Alberta border, and the Interior Salish south from Alexandria on the Fraser River.

Each tribe had individuals skilled in healing, and these people were designated as shamans. They were recognized as being able to effect cures and as having supernatural powers. They were given gifts or food. Sometimes, if a cure was not attained, the gifts were returned.

Spheres of healing were recognized in three different situations: possession by evil spirits (thought to be the cause of such medical conditions as arthritis, pneumonia, infections, tumours, stomach problems, etc.); conditions resulting from a slight or injury to a relative or friend; and demon possession. Demon possession cannot be completely explained by thinking of it as a psychosis. Individuals possessed by demons often died unless treated by a shaman. Interestingly, Dr John Willms, who spent a good many years in Africa, told me of similar beliefs and customs in the villages there.

In the tribes of central British Columbia there were individuals who were recognized as good shamans; that is, there were those who were motivated to improve people's lives. There were also evil shamans; that is, those who were feared for their perceived ability to cast spells and to send demons to possess individuals. Evil shamans seemed to be a make-work source for good shamans, who were necessary to cast out the evil spirits implanted by the former. In his or her role of expiating an injury or slight resulting from words or actions, the shaman fulfilled a role somewhat akin to that of the present-day lawyer.

There were differences in the manner in which shamans were selected. In some instances, knowledge was handed down from parent to offspring; in others, the shaman demonstrated occult power, often after days of fasting and sensory deprivation. This led to his or her being recognized as the village or tribal shaman. In 1807 Harman records that each village had a "medicine man," and this continues to be true today.

The eastern Canadian tribes had a considerable armamentarium of herbal medicines, but the central British Columbia tribes had few useful remedies. Oolichan grease was a panacea for all types of conditions: coughs, colds, pneumonia, infertility, impotence, asthenia, rheumatism, incontinence, and mental illness. It contains large amounts of vitamins D and A.

Willow bark was also used for pain, and this has some scientific basis. Salicylates are concentrated in the willow's cambium layer, and I have seen multiple small chips of bark taken from the green trunks of willow trees. For skin conditions an ointment was made of bear grease and spruce pitch; this was not a very effective salve. Burn holes were made on arthritic joints with the glowing end of burning willow sticks. This was similar to pyrofuge, a discarded European method of treatment that made use of burn therapy. In Hazelton I have seen two-centimetre wide third-degree burns result from this treatment.

Sweathouses were used for a variety of respiratory conditions. An eight-foot diameter round hut was made of bent willow-limbs covered over with skins. Rocks were heated to a red-hot intensity in a central pit, and water was poured over them. The Natives sat naked in the hut until heated, then rolled in snow or leapt into the cold water of a stream.

Most shamanic treatments involved the spirit world, and witchcraft informed a large part of them. In *The History of the Northern Interior of British Columbia* Father A.G. Morice describes the actions of a shaman in a Babine village:

> *Amidst a tremendous tumult of wailing and singing by attendants, a conjurer, dressed in furs and feathers as a spirit man, waved his personal totem rattle over the patient. He danced to the time of the music, and worked himself up into such a degree of frenzy that he seemed to possess his own particular spirit form, the image of which he directed toward the prostrate form of the patient. Then, falling suddenly on his charge, he sucked out of his or her naked body a diminutive reptile, a stick, or other impurity. (1869, p. 349)*

This "reptile...stick, or other impurity" was supposed to symbolize the material form of the cause of the illness.

In the first part of the twentieth century a Williams Lake pioneer, Patricia Mayfield, observed the actions of a shaman in the Williams Lake area.

> *Mathilda and Eddie had a very ill child likely afflicted with tuberculous meningitis. After conventional medical treatment proved to be ineffective they called in their Indian shaman.*
>
> *The shaman dressed in feathers, furs, and skins came into the baby's room blowing smoke across the infant's face and waving a rattle. Time after time he passed the rattle over the baby's body and took it to the window and shook it outside the window. Alas, the shaman had no better success than the accredited medical doctor. The baby died. (Personal communication)*

I have a personal recollection of the work of a shaman in 1957. A 17-year-old Native girl was brought to the Wrinch Memorial Hospital in Hazelton in a totally withdrawn state. The only statement that could be obtained from her was that she had seen an owl sitting on her windowsill the previous night. All tests were negative; she did not improve and seemed to be mortally stricken. A colleague, Dr Whiting, who had had considerable experience with Native people, advised me that it was a case of demon possession: a curse had been laid on her by a shaman. To my amazement it took another shaman to correct the situation.

In spite of this, I wondered about the continuing existence of the shamans. Their instruments are crude; their medicine largely ineffective for ordinary clinical conditions; and, for modern days, their bedside manner is quite bizarre. A lecture by Dr Paul Hieber, Professor of Anthropology at Trinity University in the Midwest, provided me with considerable enlightenment. The lecture was pedantic enough, and was entitled "The Household Deities of South India." Listening, I nodded until he came to the healing role of the deities. Then I sat upright. He was talking of traditional North American medicine. Dr Hieber acknowledged that Western medical doctors did well with such conditions as appendicitis, pneumonia, fractures, and surgical conditions; but he pointed out how poorly they fared with patients affected (both mentally and physically) by the traumas of everyday living. In India, through the ministrations of the household deities, these traumas were effectively managed.

The same can be said of the Native shamans; with true medical and surgical conditions they did poorly, but with stress-related diseases and demon possession they did well. In the waiting rooms of medical doctors in north-central British Columbia, almost a third of the patients are affected with conditions caused by social problems: job stress, spousal difficulties, sexual problems, discipline problems with children, and so on. The true cause of the complaint often cannot be plainly voiced, so an acceptable substitute is found and presented as the primary problem. For example, a patient's apparent problem might be stomach pain severe enough to affect work and sexual response; however, the real problem may well be abuse or crushing stresses that cannot be borne.

How poorly scientific medicine deals with these problems! How closely they are woven into the warp and weft of society. We cannot change their cause—only paint over their symptoms with medicine. The Native shaman, like the south Indian household deities, was able to deal with the roots of these problems. Unfortunately, their patients have lost faith in them due to their apparent inability to deal with medical and surgical conditions. I believe that shamans still have something to offer that white coats, stethoscopes, tranquillizers, and sleeping medications do not: a means of dealing with problems stemming from the stresses of everyday life.

CHAPTER **2**

Medical Doctors Of Barkerville In The Gold-Rush Era

The first gold found in British Columbia was on the Queen Charlotte Islands. This was long before the Cariboo Gold Rush and before either Fort Victoria or New Westminster were established. It was a small deposit, however, and did not amount to much. The first gold findings on the Mainland were in the Kamloops area, and reports of them reached Governor James Douglas in 1856. As chief factor of the Hudson's Bay Company, Governor Douglas tried to suppress this news in order to protect the Company's fur-trading business. The Hudson's Bay Company was only interested in the fur trade and did not want the vast trapping area west of the Rockies to be overrun with either gold-seekers or colonists. In 1858 gold was found on the gravel bars of the lower Fraser River; word soon spread to Fort Victoria and then to San Francisco, and the rush was on. Shipload after shipload of gold miners from California arrived at Fort Victoria, which was the initial outfitting post, and then made their way across the Strait of Georgia to the mouth of the Fraser. It was estimated that 20,000 men were on the Fraser and its tributaries by 1859. The vanguard of the crowd pushed on up the terrible and awesome Fraser Canyon or else took the alternate route via Harrison Lake, through Pemberton Meadows, and over the Coast Range to Lillooet. From there they crossed the Fraser River, went over the Pavilion Mountains, and arrived in Clinton, where they met up with those hardy souls who made it through the Fraser Canyon.

Those going up the canyon turned east at Lytton and followed the somewhat less challenging route up the Thompson River to Ashcroft. Here they turned north to Clinton. Some 150 miles further north, a few miles above the town of Williams Lake, the trail swung back to the Fraser River. There, on the bars at Soda Creek and Fort Alexandria, the miners found gold much coarser than that on the lower Fraser, which indicated to them that they were getting closer to bigger and better paydirt.

Some of them proceeded to Quesnel Mouth and up the Quesnel River, where some fairly rich ground was staked. Others turned east at Fort Alexandria and other points, making their way across country to Horsefly and Likely at the lower end of Quesnel Lake. They pushed on to Quesnel Forks and Keithley Creek, where some very good claims were developed. The appetite for gold spurred on a further intrepid group, which included Dutch Bill Dietz. This group went on past Keithley Creek (named after Doc Keithley), up over the high Snowshoe Plateau, down to Antler Creek, and eventually to Williams Creek, where they struck the fabulously rich claims that produced the millions and millions of dollars that made the Cariboo Gold Rush famous. Williams Creek was named after Dutch Bill Dietz.

Several thousand miners flocked into the area in short order. Most, of course, came up from the lower Fraser, but one band of sturdy adventurers—the Overlanders—came from eastern Canada, across the Prairies to Fort Edmonton, to Jasper House, and then through the Rockies. From Tete Jaune Cache, west of Jasper, part of the group navigated the wild upper Fraser to Fort George, then came down to Quesnelle Mouth. Some went down the North Thompson River to Kamloops, then across the Brigade Trail to Williams Creek. Some perished on both routes. The son of one of these Overlanders, C.A. Tunstall, eventually completed medical school and came back to Barkerville to practise.

Four "towns" grew up, each about a mile apart: namely, Richfield, Maryville, Williams Creek, and Camerontown. Some of the richest claims were centred around that of Billy Barker and Company, the famous claim of Cariboo Cameron being one of them. The settlement in this area became very substantial, and the name Barkerville was adopted. Eventually Barkerville grew to a population of around 30,000 and was touted to be the largest city west of Chicago and north of San Francisco. It soon attracted a variety of professionals appropriate to such a metropolis. Merchants opened up stores, a great number of saloons appeared, churches were built, lodging houses and dining rooms opened for business, and women of various sorts arrived on the scene—including the hurdy gurdy dancehall girls imported from Germany.

At a meeting of miners in 1862, it was decided that a hospital was needed. The Williams Creek Hospital (later known as the Royal Cariboo Hospital) was duly completed in 1863. It was built of logs, with two rooms for patients, a kitchen, and quarters for the steward. The steward was nurse, head cook, janitor, and bedpan washer. With the building of a hospital, doctors arrived.

Dr John Chipp arrived in Barkerville in 1863 and was put in charge of the hospital. He was English-trained and had his Master of the Royal College of Surgery (MRCS). He was also a dentist and a drugstore proprietor. Like most of the medical men who followed him, John Chipp was active in the mining industry. He had interests in several claims, and a gold commissioner's report dated December 1, 1863, stated that Chipp and Company No. 1 shaft had 12 men working and was taking out 40 to 50 ounces of gold a day. In 1869, a *Cariboo Sentinel* news item reported that Dr Chipp was moving to a new office, and, in 1872, another news item reported that he was enlarging his drugstore. In 1873, a bankruptcy notice pertaining to Dr Chipp appeared in the *Sentinel*. This did not seem to permanently hamper him, as an 1876 bill of sale is recorded for some property that he bought from Nason and Company. In 1865, the position of medical officer at the hospital seems to have been transferred from John Chipp to Thomas Bell. However, Chipp remained active in Barkerville and, on the death of Bell in 1876, he resumed the position of medical officer. He practised in Barkerville for several more years and then moved to Vernon, where he died in 1886.

Dr Thomas Bell arrived in Barkerville around 1864. He was born in England in 1822 and had his MB and his MRCS, having graduated from an English teaching hospital. He was reported to be a reliable and sober man, not as much interested in mining as were some of his colleagues. He appears to have been a capable surgeon. It was reported that he treated a man who had had his nose bitten off in a fight. Dr Bell did a graft from the arm to the nose, and the man was reported to have gone around for several weeks with his armed bandaged to his nose (I assume that he had a pedicle graft). In any case, the results of this graft were reported to have been good. Another case that Dr Bell attended (and that was reported in the *Sentinel*) concerned a man, David French, who fell 55 feet down a mineshaft when the rope holding the bucket he was riding in broke. He survived. Another accident that Dr Bell attended (again reported in the *Sentinel*) involved a man named Sprall, who fell

In
Memory
of
Dr Thomas Bell
Doctor In Charge
Royal Cariboo Hospital
Born York, England
June 8, 1822
Died Barkerville,
August 12, 1875

down the mineshaft on the Hart claim on Williams Creek in 1865. Thomas Bell continued to practise in Barkerville until he became ill with some kind of paralysis. He died in 1875. He was buried in the Barkerville cemetery, where his grave marker may still be seen.

Dr Bell's wife and family remained in England.

Dr Robert William Weir Carrall settled at Williams Creek in 1867. Born in Woodstock, Upper Canada, in 1839, he died in 1879 and was buried at the place of his birth. Robert Carrall attended Trinity College in Toronto and graduated in Medicine at McGill in 1859. He joined the Northern Army and served as a surgeon during the US civil war. He landed at Nanaimo in 1866, where he practised for a time. He travelled up the Cariboo Road to Barkerville where, in 1867, he opened a practice. Although Dr Carrall did practise medicine, he was better known for his political interests. He was, like most of his colleagues, interested in mining, and Victoria's *Daily British Colonist* reported his interest in the rich Minnehaha claim at Harvey Creek. In 1868 he was elected as the Cariboo representative in the Legislative Assembly in Victoria. He was among the delegates sent to Ottawa to negotiate British Columbia's terms for agreeing to Confederation. He was an avid supporter of Confederation, and, after British

Dr. Robert Carrall stands in the door of his one-room office in Barkerville, B.C. c.1869. Courtesy of Barkerville Heritage Museum (BHM).

Columbia joined Canada in 1871, Dr Carrall was appointed to the senate by Prime Minister John A. McDonald as a reward for his efforts. It was Robert Carrall who introduced the bill to celebrate July 1 as Dominion Day. He married E.A. Gordon shortly before his death in Ontario. Vancouver's Carrall Street, which was a busy thoroughfare at that time, was named after him.

There seems to have been, at one time or another, about a dozen doctors in the Barkerville area during the period between 1862 and 1920. A few were more prominent than were others, due either to their medical work or to their political activity. We have few details regarding a number of the earlier people, as many were not registered and the College of Physicians and Surgeons of British Columbia was not established until after the passing of the Medical Act in 1886.

A number of medical men were part of the steady stream of humanity that travelled between the gold fields and the southwest coast in Barkerville's heyday.

Dr A.W.S. Black practised mainly in New Westminster but must also have done some work in Barkerville, as he issued an 1864 invoice to the Williams Creek Hospital records for $780 for services and medicines provided. In 1863, Dr Black represented Cariboo West in the Colonial Legislative Council. He was found dead beside the road between New Westminster and Granville in 1871, and it was believed he was thrown from his horse while making a medical call.

A *Dr Brown* was also apparently in this area in 1864. We do not have details on him, but in the Royal Cariboo Hospital records in 1864 there is an invoice for $500 received by the hospital for work done and medicine provided. He was not registered with the College of Physicians and Surgeons in 1890.

Dr T.N. Foster was a Scotsman who resided in Camerontown from 1863 to 1872, but it is said that he was more interested in gold mining than in practising medicine and that he seldom charged for anything he did.

Dr W.B. Wilkinson from Upper Canada was the first surgeon in Quesnel. He was in the gold fields from 1864 to 1866 and he died at the age of 35 at Cottonwood, between Quesnel and Barkerville of unknown causes.

Dr F. Trevor was an English-trained surgeon who practised first in Quesnelle Mouth and then in Barkerville between 1863 and 1868. Reputed to have been very clever, Trevor left Barkerville in 1868, and may have practised in Quesnel. It is noted that he was appointed coroner at the same time as was Dr Bell.

Dr Siddall was an American homeopathic physician and miner present in the Barkerville gold fields in 1865. His *Cariboo Sentinel* ad on June 6 of that year read:

> *If you wish to be cured of diseases of every kind without the aid of Mercury, call Dr. Siddall, either at his office, Camerontown, or his residence, Marysville, Williams Creek.*

Dr Hugh Watt, born in Fergus, Ontario, he was the great grandson of James Watt (who invented the steam engine) and was the great uncle of Mrs Gertrude Fraser, nee Watt, of Quesnel (wife of the late Honourable Alex V. Fraser, one-time Minister of Transport and Highways). Hugh Watt received his MD from the University of Toronto and arrived in Barkerville via San Francisco in 1882. He was surgeon in charge of the hospital from 1882 to 1895. He served on the school board in Barkerville and, for one term, in the Legislature in Victoria. Based upon an announcement in a local newspaper he did not appear to be very popular as a politician.

Hugh Watt had two sons: One, Alfred T. Watt, was a medical officer at the quarantine station at William Head near Victoria. The second,

Barkerville. Dr. Hugh Watt (far left) poses with Judge Begbie and a host of other locals for one of the many photographers who went to Barkerville.
Courtesy of BHM.

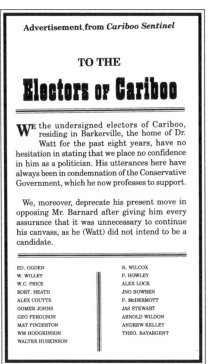

As a politician Dr Watt had a few detractors. (BCARS)

Hubert L. Watt, was a graduate of Toronto's Osgoode Hall and a successful barrister and business executive.

Hubert practised in Toronto and was later a legal advisor for Canada Life Insurance Company. He passed away in May 1913 after a lingering illness, with his father, Dr Hugh Watt, by his side. Then two months later, his brother Alfred committed suicide in a fit of depression. By 1896, Hugh Watt had left Barkerville for good and, in 1897, his ad appeared in the *Fort Steele Prospector*. He died in Fort Steele in 1914.

Dr William Rheinhard, who was a German, replaced Dr Watt as medical officer in 1892 and stayed in Barkerville until 1895.

Dr Charles Augustus (Gus) Tunstall graduated from McGill University in 1891 and registered with the College of Physicians and Surgeons of British Columbia the same year. He served as Surgeon-in-Charge of the Royal Cariboo Hospital from 1893 to 1910. "Gus," as he was called, was the son of George C. Tunstall, an Overlander who made the arduous trip from eastern Canada, across the Prairies to Fort Edmonton, to Jasper House, and then through the Rockies to the gold fields. In 1898 Gus married Alice Bowron, daughter of Gold Commissioner John Bowron. He was 29 at the time, and she was 24. The wedding took place in St Saviour's Church in Barkerville. Perusal of the hospital records indicates that Dr Tunstall was a very active and conscientious medical officer. After leaving Barkerville, he practised in Kamloops for a number of years and, in 1916, moved to Fort George. In 1931 he was believed to be practising in Australia.

Dr Michael Callanan graduated from King's and Queen's College in Ireland in 1875. He registered with the College of Physicians and

Surgeons of British Columbia in 1889 and practised initially in New Westminster, then in Quesnelle Mouth. He moved up to Barkerville in 1899, and hospital records show that he accepted a position as surgeon at the Royal Cariboo Hospital at a salary of $1,400 per year, with the privilege of carrying on his private practice "so long as it did not interfere with his hospital work." (Royal Cariboo Hospital, minutes of Trustee's meeting, 1899.) He remained in Barkerville until his death in 1927. There is a note in the records of the hospital board meeting of 1910 stating that Dr Callanan had been elected to the Legislative Assembly and would be away for two to three months but would provide a qualified MD to take his place. His replacement was Dr B.S. Smith. It is not recorded when Dr Callanan stopped practising, only that he died in 1927. He seems to have been the last resident doctor practising in Barkerville. It is known that Dr G.R. (Paddy) Baker of Quesnel used to travel by horse and buggy to Barkerville to see patients at the hospital if the town happened to be without a doctor.

Dr Walter Ashley Wilkins never practised in Barkerville but was the doctor at the famous Bullion Mine on the Quesnel River four miles below the town of Likely. He deserves mention here because he was a part of the gold-mining scene (even though this was after the main rush, there was still lots of gold around). Dr Wilkins graduated in medicine from McGill University in 1899 and registered in British Columbia the same year. In 1897 the Cariboo Hydraulic Company was incorporated and began hydraulicking the immense gold-bearing gravel banks and ancient river beds on the Quesnel River. Its camp consisted of 150 men, a power plant, a sawmill, a store, bunkhouses, a dining room, and a hospital: it was a thriving community. Dr Wilkins was the company doctor from 1899 until well into the 1900s. I do not know when he ceased to practise, but, according to the records of the College of Physicians and Surgeons of British Columbia, he died in 1962. I was interested to read in the Bullion Mine Company daily journal for December 23, 1901, that a call came for Dr Wilkins from Polley's Lake (10 miles away) at 3:00 AM. Alex Tingley, a mine company teamster, hitched the horses to a sleigh and they left at 3:15 AM to make the call.

When the peak of the gold-mining activity started to drop off in the 1870s, the crowd moved on and the need for medical services diminished. We see that, in 1873, Dr Hugh Watt was after the provincial government for a subsidy to keep him in the area, as he could not make a living from private practice. I note that, according to one early account, the doctor in Quesnel had to resort to farming to help make ends meet. (Some later surgeons have tried to convince the Internal Revenue Department that they too were farmers, but with limited success!)

The doctor who held the position of hospital surgeon at the Royal Cariboo Hospital was a little better off than most—but not much. His contract usually stipulated that, out of his salary, he was to supply the medicines needed. The Royal Cariboo Hospital had to continually fight with the government in Victoria for funds, in spite of the millions of dollars in taxes and royalties that were collected from the area. The situation is unchanged today, 100 years later. If anything, it is worse. A century ago there seems to have been a well organized hospital board, and relations between the hospital surgeon and the latter appear to have been quite amicable. At times the surgeon had to bring to the attention of the board conditions that he thought should be rectified. One such condition is recorded in the board minutes, wherein a letter from the doctor protested the hospital steward preparing corpses for burial. The steward looked after the patients and cooked their meals, and the doctor thought that having him do this other work was a "moral and sanitary crime." He asked that the undertaker be delegated to carry out this chore. On another occasion the doctor requested a new stretcher for the hospital, as when a woman who was injured asked to borrow a stretcher the only one they could find was a broken-down old wreck that they used for carrying corpses.

The pace of medical practice was not great at that time, and 24-hour medical service was neither available nor expected. We see that at a hospital board meeting in 1902 Dr Callanan asked permission to go to Quesnel to assist at a surgical operation. This would require four to five days by horse for the return trip. On another occasion, in 1907, he informed the board that he had been subpoenaed to attend the assize court in Clinton as an expert witness and would be away for two weeks. He had arranged for the doctor from Quesnel to cover urgent cases.

In Dr C.A. Tunstall's annual report to the hospital board in 1899, it was indicated that the total number of patient days for the year was 548. Average length of stay was 42 days. The caseload that the doctor had to contend with included injuries of all sorts, which was not surprising, considering that the mining activities below the canyon on William's Creek required shafts to be dug 50 to 80 feet deep in order to get down to paydirt. Working in these deep holes was hazardous. Infections of various kinds were encountered—everything from "la Grippe" (flu) to tertiary syphilis, pneumonia, malaria (brought up from Panama), consumption (tuberculosis), mountain fever, frostbite, melancholia, and retention of urine.

None of these doctors became rich, either from gold-mining activities or from practising medicine. They were, after all, adventurers—the same as were all the others who ventured into this previously uncharted region. They took life as it came and did their best for their fellow human beings. Unemployment insurance, tenure, and cushy pensions were not part of their system. Some who entered politics fared better than did those who simply practised medicine. Dr Robert Carrall, by accepting an appointment to the Senate in Ottawa, came up with the ultimate solution to his pension problems.

CHAPTER **3**

The Lasting Legacy of Dr Robert Tomlinson: Ankitlas and the Kispiox Area

Dr Robert Tomlinson, 1840-1913.
(BCARS B-07583)

The first Western-trained doctors came to the central Interior's gold fields at Barkerville in the 1860s. Three hundred miles to the north and west lay an isolated area along the Skeena and Kispiox Rivers. Here, very primitive living conditions prevailed; there was no spiritual guidance and little medical care for the inhabitants. This was to change in 1879, when Dr Robert Tomlinson arrived on the scene.

Only one doctor in British Columbia had an 8,050-foot peak bearing his family name. Dr Tomlinson has both Mount Tomlinson in north-central British Columbia and an area along the Kispiox

River called Tomlinson's Flats named for him. He is also remembered as someone who manufactured bricks that, after over 100 years, are still in good condition.

Through the years I have been intrigued by the name Tomlinson without ever really knowing the history of its bearer. Apparently he was, for four years, a doctor and medical missionary to the Tsimshian living near Kispiox village, which is located in the triangle between the junction of the Kispiox and Skeena Rivers. Prior to this he had served 12 years along the northern coast and had spent several years with William Duncan at Metlakatla.

The man and his family endured incredible hardships to bring medical knowledge and spiritual guidance to the Natives of British Columbia. He arrived in the Kispiox area in 1879, together with his wife and four children, two horses, a cow, and a bull. This meant an overland trek of 120 miles through the Nass River country during spring runoff, with the torment of flies, insects, and marauding bears.

In addition to the above hazards, Tomlinson's wife Alice became ill with typhoid fever, necessitating three weeks of lay-over on the trail. There is every likelihood that they would have starved to death had not a Native woman bearing a sack of potatoes found them and given them succour.

Dr Robert Tomlinson, born in 1840, came from a prominent family in Dublin, Ireland, where his father was the presiding Protestant minister in a large church. One brother was a doctor with the British army. Robert Tomlinson studied medicine at Dublin University and spent a year of internship at Adelaide Hospital in Dublin—a hospital that is still in existence. Dr R.G. Large, in *Skeena: River of Destiny*, states that Tomlinson purposely omitted writing his final exams so as to avoid the temptation to practise medicine full time. According to the College of Physicians and Surgeons of British Columbia, he was not registered in BC.

Following internship at Adelaide in 1867, Tomlinson answered an inward call to engage in missionary activity on the northern coast of British Columbia. Later, with wife and family, he journeyed to Metlakatla, a Christian Native village on the BC coast that had maintained its identity by separating itself from the Native community at Port Simpson. It was Robert Tomlinson's dream to establish a similar Christian Native community in the Kispiox area. Like at Metlakatla, the Natives would be strictly supervised, there would be neither drinking nor gambling, and schooling and medical care would be established.

Native Spirit Totems, Kispiox
Shamans tried to undermine Dr Tomlinson's efforts.
Courtesy of Jessie Gould.

The Tomlinsons' arrival at Kispiox in 1879 was not without hazard. Mrs Tomlinson was so frightened at having to cross the Native bridge over the Bulkley River at Hagwilget that she crawled its entire length. This was a bridge constructed of wire left over from the abandoned Collins Overland Telegraph Line in 1866. It was a cantilevered structure consisting of poles and logs, and it spanned the raging torrent of the Bulkley River.

Their reception at the Kispiox village was not auspicious. Their bull drowned attempting to swim the river, and their mare kicked one of the Native's dogs, breaking its leg—an action that required negotiation and recompense. In addition, the local shamans were opposed to the Tomlinsons' presence. The result was that the Tomlinson family moved seven miles further into the wilderness and established a small settlement along the banks of the Kispiox River. This settlement was called Ankitlas, which means "place where bark is peeled." It was 17 miles from Hazelton, which, at that time, was called The Forks.

The Tomlinsons lived in a tent structure placed on a log foundation. Medicine was dispensed with the patients lodged in either the Tomlinsons' abode or in accessible space in other homes. On occasion cots were placed in the salmon smokehouses. Home visits

Mount Tomlinson on the left.
Courtesy of Marjorie Lee.

often meant that Dr Tomlinson had to be away from his family for one or two days at a time.

Dr Tomlinson's medical work seemed to be more surgical than otherwise. He was in constant conflict with the shamans, who, for the most part, tried to undermine his work. His son, writing later, tells of a Native who was severely mauled by a grizzly bear. Dr Tomlinson was called to visit the injured man, who had been brought down the mountain straddled on the neck of a carrier. He found the injuries to be severe—laceration of the scalp, a hand-sized bite taken from the thigh muscle, the ends of the right lower ribs bitten through and severed, and numerous other lacerations together with shock and blood loss.

The father of the unfortunate young man suspected witchcraft and was decked out in war paint, ready to do the evil shaman in, when Tomlinson halted him and made him promise to refrain from taking any such actions. He also made him promise not to call in any shamans. For five hours, in a salmon smokehouse, Dr Tomlinson worked on the young man. The patient recovered, and this was a great boon to Tomlinson's work.

There is little record of maternity cases, except that, during their four-year stay in the Kispiox area, Dr Tomlinson delivered two of his own children. Village babies were delivered by Native midwives.

In January 1881, on an extremely cold day, a call was received requesting medical aid for a Native man who had been shot during a potlatch at Kispiox. Dr Tomlinson dared not take any more than one blanket from his home because there was scant bedding available, and, after snowshoeing seven miles to Kispiox and caring for his patient, he was not able to return to Ankitlas. He remained in a largely unheated building at Kispiox and survived only because of the press of a number of mongrel dogs who, like him, were seeking as much warmth as possible. For years afterward Dr Tomlinson suffered the effects of freezing.

Meanwhile, the work at the Tomlinson community proceeded apace. A number of Native families moved to join it and avail themselves of a Christian atmosphere, schooling, and medical care.

Dr Tomlinson performed complicated surgery
in these smokehouses.

Babies were born, families were raised, and children were
schooled in houses like these.
Courtesy of Jessie Gould.

A school was established, at which Mrs Tomlinson and Dr Tomlinson's brother Edward taught, and the foundation of a hospital was laid in this isolated area along the Kispiox River.

It was at this point that bureaucracy reared its head. The Anglican bishop, Dr Ridley, ruled that Dr Tomlinson was to abandon his work on the Kispiox River and move into Hazelton to serve the Native people and miners who congregated there. This was probably a sensible move (and one that Dr Wrinch, some 20 years later, was to make on his own), but Dr Tomlinson, with an obstinacy that was probably part of his character, decided to appeal the decision to the Anglican Church Missionary Society in London.

Tomlinson left his family in the Kispiox area, trekked 120 miles to the Nass River (on snowshoes), journeyed across Canada by rail, across the ocean, and finally arrived in England. Once there, his appeal to the Church Missionary Society was approved. He then went to Ireland on a fund-raising venture, where he was able to visit his father and speak in his church in Dublin. He also re-established contact with his brother, a surgeon with the British army in India. Later, recounting this experience, Tomlinson mentioned that, in Kispiox, he had treated more bullet wounds than his brother had in India.

Dr Tomlinson then made his way by degrees back to Hazelton and Kispiox, but he found that his relationship with his bishop had deteriorated and that his work could no longer be continued.

With a heavy heart he closed up his mission, abandoned the hospital, and, in the spring of 1883, made his way over scattered patches of ice in the Skeena River to the coast and to Metlakatla. Mrs Tomlinson was by then pregnant with her seventh child, two having been born at Ankitlas in the Kispiox Valley.

In 1920 Tomlinson's son, Robert Tomlinson Jr, was employed at the Hazelton hospital and recorded the history of his family's stay in the Kispiox Valley. He found monuments to his father's work in the form of Mount Tomlinson and Tomlinson's Flats on the Kispiox River, and he was amazed to find that some of the bricks laid by his father were still in good repair. In spite of their difficulties the Tomlinsons had endured, and the medical treatment and spirituality they had offered the people of Kispiox was still remembered.

Dr Tomlinson died in 1913, after many years of difficult service. His four-year stay in the isolated Kispiox Valley, while beset with hardships and tragedy, left its mark. It is only fitting that an 8,050-foot peak bears his name.

CHAPTER 4

Alice Tomlinson:
Debutante Wife of Dr Tomlinson

Alice Tomlinson
(BCARS A-02496)

In St Louis, Missouri, gateway to the territory, there is a statue of a pioneer woman, child in hand, looking steadfastly west, where, in the 1860s, lay the wilderness. Like her, the real heroes of the families in central British Columbia were the doctors' wives, who faced hardships and dangers with unflinching courage and resolution.

The early doctors were drawn by gold to the Barkerville fields. Conditions were so primitive in the 1860s that their wives did not accompany them. Thomas Bell's wife and children remained in England and never did come to Canada. His burial spot in the Barkerville cemetery is marked by a 100-year-old white spruce, and there is no evidence of recognition from his family overseas. Dr Hugh Watt, an early doctor in the Barkerville area, did not bring his wife to Barkerville, likely because of the crude conditions and lack of accommodations.

The earliest wife to come to the wilderness frontier was Alice Woods Tomlinson, who came to the north coast of British Columbia in 1867 and, in 1897, followed her husband to an isolated Kispiox medical mission field. Her story is particularly fascinating. She was the privileged younger daughter in a prominent Victoria family. Dr R.G. Large, in *Skeena: River of Destiny*, describes her wedding to a penurious peripatetic Irish medical missionary, Robert Tomlinson. In the few days prior to the wedding, a stretch of road was built through an undeveloped treed area to provide better access to the reception site. Alice had five bridesmaids. It would seem that the Reverend Dr Tomlinson was quite impatient to return to his mission field appointment at Metlakatla and was not pleased that the elaborate wedding preparations necessitated delaying the wedding for five days.

Alice Tomlinson would prove to be a tower of strength to her impatient, energetic husband, whom she steadied through many difficult situations over the next 45 years. Letters from the Tomlinsons' son, Robert Jr, describe their life in north-central British Columbia. The first 12 years were spent amongst the coast tribes, where the Tomlinsons ministered to the souls and the physical needs of the Tsimshian. During this time Alice Tomlinson endured very primitive living conditions and bore her first four children. At this time there were no elaborate birthing units with sophisticated nurseries. A wife literally went to the edge with each child and entered into labour with the sure knowledge that she must deliver that baby or die trying. There were no such things as analgesics for pain, blood transfusions, antibiotics, or medicines for uterine relaxation; and if things went badly awry, there was no possibility of emergency evacuation. The women lay in their beds in rude log cabins, clenched their teeth on a roll of cloth at the height of their pain, and clung to midwives and husbands. Breast milk was the main source of a baby's nourishment, and a mother with a poor supply often lost her infant. In addition, the household tasks had to be accomplished without the help of washing machines, dishwashers, or electric stoves.

Eighteen seventy-nine found the Tomlinsons living in Ankitlas on the Kispiox River, 17 miles north of Hazelton. Their vision was to build a village safe from the vices of drink and gambling, and this is what they did. Mrs Tomlinson carried a considerable part of the workload. Her home, which consisted of four rows of logs covered by a tent, was opened for church services, for teaching Native children

The Kispiox church eventually took on new dimensions long after
Alice Tomlinson held services in her own tent home.
(BCARS I-21900)

to read and write, and for offering counselling to Native people. Three
services were held in this crude living structure each Sunday, with
the last one being held in the evening.

Dr Tomlinson carried on the construction of the village, the
preaching, and the practice of medicine. Mrs Tomlinson cared for
her family; performed the usual household tasks of washing, cooking,
and cleaning; and helped Dr Tomlinson with surgery, giving
anaesthetics and nursing care, in spite of not having had formal
nurses' training. In addition to this she had to make due with crude
household implements, a cranky poorly heating kitchen stove, and
an indifferent wood supply, which made it difficult to maintain any
sort of heat in the house.

During the Tomlinsons' four-year stay at Ankitlas, Mrs Tomlinson
was pregnant three times and bore two children—her fifth and sixth
child, respectively. Many years later, Robert Tomlinson Jr (1953)
wrote of his sister's delivery in January of 1880. In his letter to his
sister Annie, he says:

> *You may not know it, but you were born in the*
> *stable. That day God showed his hand. For days the*
> *thermometer had been way below zero, 30 degrees or*
> *more. The day you were born it rose to 32 degrees*
> *above zero Fahrenheit, the freezing point. We were*
> *living in an unfinished large log house. We had only*
> *one heating stove. The cook stove gave out very little*
> *heat and we were huddled around the heater, which*
> *took three foot lengths of wood.*

When the time came that you were to join us it
was decided to fix up a canvas like a tent under the
roof in the barn. The tent was made ready, a large
bonfire was kept burning on the outside to keep the
inside of the tent warm enough for your arrival. One
of the troubles was that the heat from the fire melted
the snow on the roof. There was a continual dripping
of water between the fire and the tent. They were
afraid the snow would slide off the roof and put the
fire out. Poor mother, how did she stand it? Anyway,
everything turned out all right. The day after you
were born the temperature dropped below 40 degrees
below zero.

In February 1882 Alice Tomlinson gave birth to Edward Sterling, her sixth child. The house was warmer at that time, and the danger from the cold much less than it had been at Annie's birth. However, the baby's cradle was made of skins covering a small base of wood, and it was suspended from the ceiling. When the baby was about six months old and resting in this crude cradle, the ties on one end became loosened and he came crashing to the floor. He died soon afterwards from a fractured skull.

The whole family was stricken with grief, particularly Mrs Tomlinson, who felt responsible for the accident. However, family and friends came together and the tragedy was surmounted. A small grave was dug on the edge of the Kispiox River, and a small wooden marker indicated the place. Later, this was replaced with a stone and a small enclosing fence. A friend from Victoria, Emily Woods, painted a picture of the grave and penned these words below it: "One amidst the forest of the west by a dark stream is laid. The Indian knows his place of rest, far in the pine tree shade."

The Tomlinsons endured a further two years, six months of which Dr Tomlinson spent in Britain and Ireland. Mrs Tomlinson cared for her family of five children, maintained the settlement, and ministered to the ailing. Food consisted mainly of salmon (both smoked and fresh) caught in the Kispiox River, wild game, and produce from the vegetable garden. Sugar and flour were brought in from outside on the rare freighting vessels.

Robert Tomlinson Jr tells how each child had been encouraged to save a little sugar every week to be made into candy at Christmas time. However, as Mrs Tomlinson began the candy-making, a Native woman came with many troubles. In ministering to her, Mrs

Tomlinson forgot the home-made candy, and the sugary concoction was badly burned, much to the distress of the children.

In spite of heroic efforts, the Tomlinsons' vision of a separate village, free from the temptations of Hazelton and Kispiox, did not come into being. The planned hospital, meeting hall, and church remained a dream, although a brick-making factory continued for some time. Finally, the Tomlinsons could no longer maintain their settlement and, in the spring of 1883, made the 200-mile trip down the Skeena River. The upper reaches of this river were covered with ice floes, and Robert Jr mentions that his father, with great gentleness and care, helped Alice, who was then pregnant with her seventh child, over the ice floes from one canoe to another.

The love and dedication of this remarkable woman is almost beyond comprehension. A well-born, happy young woman from a magnificent urban home left everything to follow her husband into the wilds. Under the most trying conditions she endured and reached out to others, offering nursing, educational, and spiritual skills. Eight-thousand-and-fifty-foot Mount Tomlinson can be said to commemorate Alice Tomlinson as much as it does Robert Tomlinson.

CHAPTER 5

Horace Cooper Wrinch: Missionary Doctor Of Hazelton

Horace Cooper Wrinch.
Photo by Marjorie Lee.
Courtesy of Wrinch Memorial Hospital, Hazelton.

Seventeen years after the Tomlinsons, a permanent medical doctor came to the Hazelton area. Horace Cooper Wrinch was a large man, but his physical size was overshadowed by his accomplishments. He was a talented physician and surgeon, an agriculturalist, an architect, a statesman, and an administrator. The main motivating factor in his life was his belief in Christianity and, in particular, his strong desire to help others.

In 1957 I spoke to one of his early nurses, who had returned to the Hazelton area on a brief visit. She told a story concerning Dr Wrinch and his dedication to his patients. During her time at the hospital in the 1920s, Dr Wrinch received a call from the Native village of Kitwanga some 30 miles to the west. Apparently a Native woman had developed severe abdominal pain, was very weak, and in shock. This was during February: there was a foot of snow on the ground and the river was covered with ice.

In the darkness of early morning Dr Wrinch took his dog team and headed for Kitwanga, starting out on the river ice and portaging overland as necessary. He arrived at Kitwanga, stabilized the young woman, placed her on his sleigh, and made his way back over the river ice. Arriving at the hospital in the early evening, he stopped briefly for nourishment and then took the young woman straight into the operating room.

A misplaced pregnancy was responsible for the young woman's internal bleeding. This was removed, the abdominal cavity cleared of blood, and three litres of saline solution placed in her abdomen. This last procedure was considerably in advance of its time: although now common, replacement of lost blood with salt solutions was not widely advocated in the early part of the century. The young woman did well, and Dr Wrinch was back at his hospital duties by 6:00 AM the next day, having risen at his usual time of 5:00 AM for his morning devotions.

What was the basis for his remarkable stamina and dedication? Horace Cooper Wrinch, born in 1866 to Leonard and Elizabeth Wrinch of Kirby, England, in Essex County, was the fourth of 10 children. He received his high-school education at Albert Memorial College in Flamington, Suffolk, and, at age 14, came with his family first to Quebec and then to rural Ontario.

When settled in Ontario he finished high school and worked as a casual labourer on nearby farms. He found that he was interested in farming, and he proceeded to attend the Ontario Agricultural College for four years. He graduated from this institution with honours and with the Governor-General's Medal.

At this time his life was placid and serene. He had his own farm in Ontario and was engaged to a very devout young Methodist woman. It was her influence that helped Horace Wrinch form the resolve to be of service to his fellow human beings. He decided that the best way to do this was as a medical missionary, and so he left his farm and took a premedical course at Albert College, then going on to attend medical school at Trinity College at the University of Toronto.

As he was taking his medical school training his fiance, who was already a teacher and a deaconess in the Methodist Church, took formal nurses' training in order to be a suitable helpmate for her medical missionary husband. Upon graduation Dr Wrinch took postgraduate courses in Boston and Toronto, and he and his fiance were married, having decided to go to West China. However, they were not absolutely committed to going to China, as they were ready to go wherever they were most needed.

As luck would have it, they were most need in the interior of north-central British Columbia at the Native village of Kispiox. In 1899 Dr Wrinch and his bride boarded a CPR passenger train and made their way to Vancouver and then by ship (the *Prince George*) to Port Simpson, a village close to Prince Rupert. They spent the winter at nearby Port Essington, both actively engaged in their work as medical missionaries. Alice Wrinch worked in the small village both as a nurse and as a teacher, while Horace Wrinch worked as a doctor.

In the spring of 1900 they loaded a Native canoe and, in nine weeks, covered the 190 miles from Port Essington to Kispiox. This was no small feat, since in the spring the Skeena River has many whirlpools, rapids, and perverse currents. How this farm boy from Ontario and his deaconess bride navigated this stretch of treacherous water is a mystery. There is no indication that they had any particular skills in canoeing, so they must have been the object of considerable grace from above.

One has to appreciate the delight of these two young people, still on their honeymoon, as they made their way upstream on the Skeena. On either side were high mountains, snow-crested, their lower levels covered with alpine meadows. Along the river banks were pine, cedar, and hemlock. Each day must have required the makings of a camp, and here one cannot ignore such things as insects. The curse of central BC is mosquitos, gnats, noseeums, deer flies, and horseflies. Nine weeks in the company of these clouds of insects might be described as nine weeks of intense misery, but there was no mention of this in Dr Wrinch's records. In addition to the insects, black bears were often a nuisance, particularly if food was stored around the camp. These two babes in the woods were not deterred, finally arriving at the village of Kispiox, where they were greeted by the residents and Reverend Pierce.

Kispiox, a Native village in the Skeena District, is located on the tongue of land between the junction of the Kispiox and Skeena Rivers. It is about 10 miles from the village of Hazelton (previously called The Forks), which, in turn, is located between the Bulkley and Skeena

Kispiox Village, Dr Wrinch's first charge.
Courtesy of Jessie Gould.

Rivers. Interestingly enough, Hazelton was the terminus for steamboats plying the Skeena River from Prince Rupert to Hazelton. It is a mystery why Dr and Mrs Wrinch did not take the steamboat rather than hazard the journey in a Native canoe.

In Kispiox, which was a fairly typical Native village of that time, there were a number of small log homes dotting the landscape. There was no running water, no electricity, and no sewage disposal system. The Winches were fortunate to find a new log home, where they lived, set up a medical office, and dispensed drugs. Later, a lean-to was built onto to their home and served as a treatment room complete with surgical facilities.

Dr Wrinch was busy not only taking care of villagers, but also making calls to Hazelton (10 miles away), Glenvowel (the Salvation Army village four miles away), and also to settlers scattered along the Kispiox and Skeena Rivers. No call for help was left unanswered. Even in the midst of winter Dr Wrinch donned snowshoes and, with his medical bag being carried by his St Bernard "Rover," left to visit patients who might be a day's journey from Kispiox.

One can well imagine the joy and relief experienced by isolated settlers as they saw the tall, broad-shouldered form of Dr Wrinch snowshoeing along the stream towards their rude dwellings. His confident, cheery manner did more to make people well than did his medicines.

Meanwhile Mrs Wrinch spent a good deal of time teaching and attending to nursing duties in the village. It must have been a lonely time for this young woman from Ontario, but her quiet, cheerful manner never flagged.

In 1901 Dr Wrinch wrote his medical examinations in Vancouver. This was not as simple a matter as was taking a bus to Trinity College and writing his examinations. Kispiox was 700 miles from his destination, and he had to snowshoe 120 miles to the Nass River, take a canoe from there to Tidewaters, and then take a steamer to Vancouver. Upon successfully completing his examinations, he made his way back to Hazelton.

In 1903 Dr Wrinch felt that his work could be better and more efficiently undertaken from Hazelton, which had a larger population than did Kispiox and was central to several other villages. With considerable energy, and utilizing his experience as a builder in Ontario, he drew up plans for a 20-bed hospital—a facility that was officially opened in 1904. Not being content with this, Dr Wrinch called upon his agricultural experience and laid out extensive gardens and fruit beds in order to supply the needs of the hospital. In addition, a dairy was established to supply milk, cream, and butter.

Of considerable interest was Dr Wrinch's next venture, which was to establish a school of nursing—an institution that, for a time, was the only school of nursing west of Winnipeg. This school offered a three-year course, and the nurses received both didactic and practical experience—the first from Matron Alice Wrinch, RN (followed by Matrons Eva Hogan, RN, E.M. Bligh, RN; and A. Mathieson, RN RRC) and Dr Wrinch (who provided lectures in Medicine and Surgery) and the second from the patients in the hospital. The nursing school was in operation until 1932—28 years in all. The graduates were well trained and, according to the provincial examinations, usually placed in the top 25 of the 200 or so student nurses graduating in British Columbia.

Beginning in 1904, Dr Wrinch made an annual report for the Hazelton hospital. This report dealt with the staff, the nurses in training, and the members of the advisory board. It offered a general statement on the operations of the hospital; information regarding staff comings and goings; a section detailing volunteer donations and assistance; and, finally, the statistics for each year (the heart of the report). These statistics included the number of medical cases, surgical cases, and maternity deliveries as well as the numbers of Occidental, Chinese, Japanese, and Native patients. Statistics also indicated sex of patients; patients discharged cured, improved, or unimproved; number of deaths; causes of death; residence; country of birth; and religion (it was noted that the Anglicans predominated

Dr. Wrinch's Year End Report
Hazelton Hospital 1923

RESIDENCE

Andimaual 1	Francois Lake 4	Nanaimo 1
Bulkley Valley 1	Glen Vowell 10	Pacific 2
Bulkley Vanyon 2	Hazelton 56	Prince Rupert 2
Bear Lake 2	South Hazelton 3	Port Simpson 2
Babine 7	Hugwilget 4	Port Essington 1
Copper City 2	New Hazelton 13	Smithers 5
Cedarvale 5	Hanall 8	Terrace 21
Carnaby 1	Kishpiax 35	Telkwa 4
Doreen 3	Kitwanga 24	Tramville 1
Edmonton 1	Kitzegucla 6	Usk 15
Fraser lake 5	Meanskinisht 1	Vanderhoof.............. 3
Fort Fraser 1	Moricetown 7	Woodcock 3

COUNTRY OF BIRTH

England 25	Canada 189	China 1
Ireland 7	United States 11	Norway.................... 4
Scotland 6	France 3	Sweden 5
Wales 2	Belgium 1	Bulgaria 2
Australia 1	Germany 3	

RELIGION

Church of England ... 86	Roman Catholic 53	Presbyterian 28
Methodist 50	Baptist 4	Buddhist................. 1
Lutheran 10	Latter Day Saints 2	Salvation Army 12
Evangelist 1	Greek Church 3	None given 8

CAUSES OF DEATH

Albumenuric Toxaemia, Broncho-pneumonia, Cardiac Dilation, Coxalgia, Eclampsia, Foetid Bronchitis, General Peritonitis, Inanition, Miliary Tuberculosis, Myocarditis, Nephritis, Pneumonia, Pleurisy and Pneumonia, Tubercular Osteitis.

DISEASES TREATED

Appendicitis, appendiceal abscess, arterio-sclerosis, appendicitis and cancer, abortion, axe cut feet, axe cut shin, axe cut toes, arm amputation, abscess neck, abscess scalp, bedsore, bronchitis, broncho-pneumonia, bullet wound leg, cerebral tumor, cerebral hemorrhage, cervical adenitis, cardiac asthenia, conjunctivitis, coxalgia, concussion brain, contusion ribs, crushed finger, cystitis, dysphagia, syspepsia, dislocated shoulder, diarrhoea, debility, dilatation bladder, eczema, eclampsia, enteritis, epilepsy, emesis, gravidarum, erysipelas, foreign body in ear, flexion uterus, fractures of fibula, clavicle, pelvis, skull, femur; frostbite hands, furunculosis, gastritis, gastro-enteritis, grip, gangrene neck, gonorrhoeal arthritis, granular lids, hydatids of uterus.

First Hazelton Hospital, 1904.
Courtesy of Jessie Gould.

Dr Wrinch and student nurses
c. 1914, Hazelton.
Courtesy of Jessie Gould.

through the years, with non-Christians holding last place at one per year. Finally, Dr Wrinch's report included a financial statement showing receipts, disbursements, and final balance.

During my stay at Hazelton I was able to review the annual reports as far back as 1906 through to 1914 (there appear to be no reports between 1959 to the present). I remember noting the number of bullet wounds indicated in the 1914 report—four. This seemed to be an excessive number of bullet wounds, but, of course, it represented the great New Hazelton bank robbery.

Jessie Gould, who is bright and active at age 88, was living in New Hazelton at the time of the bank robbery and remembers it well. In 1995 she described the April morning on which the bank robbery took place. It was a damp morning, and she and her mother were washing clothes. There was an initial volley of gun shots and then a reverberating volley of dozens and dozens more. Her mother told her to lie on the floor and not to go outside. At the end of the shooting two bank robbers lay dead, one mortally wounded and three others wounded to a lesser extent. A bank clerk, John McQueen, was shot in the head by the robber's but survived. A photograph shows a sombre Dr Wrinch in attendance, as the wounded were hauled away to the hospital in a wagon. The dead were taken in hand by the police.

In 1907 a balcony was formed along the southern exposure of the hospital. This was light and airy and provided an ideal ward for patients with tuberculosis. Unfortunately there were a number of these, as tuberculosis was a scourge of both Natives and Whites in this isolated area.

In 1910 Dr Wrinch was ordained as a minister of the Methodist Church, which ratified his role as a missionary. Prior to any serious surgery he always knelt in prayer with his staff. Jessie Gould records the words of his prayer: "A human life is in our hands. We must have God's help if we are to do our best work. Let us pray together for His help."

It is difficult to imagine the hardships that were experienced by this pioneer family. Roads were incredibly rough and narrow, often little more than trails. In the spring and summer months there were mud and myriads of insects, and in the winter there were snow and ice. Dr Wrinch used a team and cutter in winter and, if the call were from a distance, engaged a driver. He snatched as much sleep and rest as he could by wrapping himself in robes on a bed of hay located in the cutter. This covering, along with heated rocks, kept him warm,

Dr Wrinch and grateful patient.
Hazelton, c. 1906.
Courtesy of Jessie Gould.

and, on his arrival at the patient's home, he was fit and ready to care for whoever was ailing. Sometimes these calls would take him away for several days, during which time the hospital was in the hands of the nursing superintendent, the nursing students, and Mrs Wrinch.

I asked Jessie Gould what sort of a man Dr Wrinch was. She remembers him as a large man who usually wore a hat outside of the hospital. He had a commanding presence but was friendly and open. He disciplined himself and applied the same discipline to his management of the hospital and his home. She was a patient of his and remembers him being very gentle in managing the disability resulting from a congenital dislocation of her hip.

Dr Wrinch had a saying, "Every respectable girl a nurse," but it was obvious that Jessie would not be a nurse because of her hip problem. He said,"Jessie, my girl, we won't make a nurse of you, but you can do many things that a nurse cannot do." Her suffering and disability gave a special sensitivity to the needs of others—a sensitivity that a regular nurse might not have. And indeed she did. She has been active in her community for over 80 years.

The earliest annual report of Hazelton Hospital that I have is for the year 1921. I noted that, under staff, Dr Wrinch is listed as medical superintendent, while Dr Hogan is listed as anaesthetist and assistant physician. E.M. Bligh was matron and superintendent of the nurses' training school, and Miss Alcoat was night superintendent of the hospital. There were also a secretary and a housekeeper. Under nurses in training are listed: third year—Mrs E. McClutcheon, affiliating in Vancouver General Hospital, and also Miss King and Miss Bates; second year—Miss Nock and Miss Mayer; first year— Miss McCall and Miss Bolivar. Under staff changes it was noted that Cupid had been interfering with the nurses' training school. An affiliate did not complete her course, and a promising student left at the end of her first year of training. A final philosophic note says,

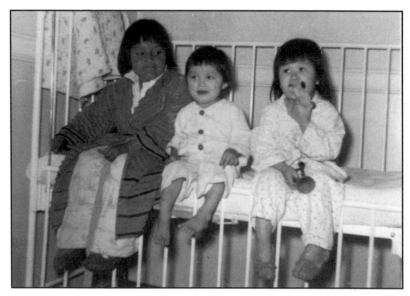

Health care of native children was a special concern.
Courtesy of Jessie Gould.

"Trifles of that nature are not allowed to interfere with the work of the Hazelton Hospital."

Under statistics, it is noted that 236 patients were admitted during 1921, 89 surgeries performed, and 29 babies delivered. There were only two Chinese and/or Japanese admitted, and Mr Don Yip, a member of a pioneer family, told me that the Chinese preferred their own herbal remedies and treatments to anything that might be found in hospitals.

Patient residence was noted, and these people came from all up and down the Grand Trunk Pacific line (which had been built in 1914). Country of birth was noted: there were 2 from Austria, 26 from England, 3 from Italy, 1 from Japan, 1 from China, 11 from Scotland, 17 from the United States, and 147 from Canada.

Under religion the Church of England again predominated, with the Methodist Church and the Roman Catholic Church following. Of comfort was that fact that only one non-Christian was admitted during the year. The cause of the nine reported deaths were detailed: two were due to apoplexy, one to typhoid fever, one to ascending paralysis, two to pneumonia, one to multiple sarcoma, one to chronic pancreatitis, and one to cardiac dropsy. It would seem that three of the nine deaths might have been prevented with modern antibiotic therapy.

In 1923 Dr Wrinch lost his loving wife and helpmate of 24 years to cancer. This was a severe blow, from which he never recovered. His wife was buried at the fore-portion of the escarpment on which the Hazelton cemetery is laid. The inscription, which is in good repair to this day, reads: "In affection and remembrance, Alice Jane Breckon, dearly beloved wife of Horace Cooper Wrinch." And underneath there is a statement of reluctant acceptance: "Thy will be done."

After this, Dr Wrinch devoted less time and energy to the management of the hospital and the practice of medicine. His son Leonard, the eldest of his five children, took over his practice and the management of the hospital, and Dr Wrinch was nominated to the BC Legislature as a Liberal candidate. He was returned to this position for the following 10 years. In 1928 he showed his concern for the future by introducing a health insurance bill that later passed into law. At that time plans were made for a second Hazelton Hospital, which was opened in 1930 and which later bore the name Wrinch Memorial Hospital. This building had 51 beds as well as modern plumbing, electricity, and heating. X-ray facilities, which had been present in the older hospital, were updated for the new one. The reputation and excellence of the hospital was recognized at the World Hospitals Convention in 1931, as the Hazelton Hospital was chosen as one of the ten best hospitals in Canada.

From 1931 to his retirement in 1936, Dr Wrinch could be compared with a great king salmon making its way up the Skeena River. After a valiant effort it reaches home sands and then, its work completed, loses ground to the rapid stream. Slowly it drifts back, growing weaker and weaker and finally, unable to hold its position, it turns on its side and the current drifts it to its final resting place.

So it was with Dr Wrinch. He retired, moved back to Ontario for a year but found it not to his liking, and, with his health deteriorating, he moved back to Vancouver. After a year, in which his health failed completely, death came on October 19, 1939. He was survived by his second wife, whom he married in 1928, one daughter, and four sons (one of whom was a doctor).

New Hazelton's *Omineca Herald* of October 25, 1939, in telling of Horace Wrinch's death, said that he was probably the most influential and best-loved man that had ever blessed the district with his presence. He won the affection and respect of his fellow citizens through his service, his kindness, and his outstanding ability as a leader and minister. He was a friend in time of need. The Kispiox village honoured Dr Wrinch by having two elders tell of his arrival as a medical missionary. They were proud of the fact that they were the first to ask for him and that it was to their village that he first came.

So passed from the scene a man of tremendous accomplishments, faithful to the Lord's admonition to love and to serve one's fellow human beings. Not for him the comfort of a settled existence in Ontario. He challenged the rugged interior of British Columbia and came forth a victor. Truly, he loved his people even more than he loved himself.

History Of Wrinch Memorial Hospital
Hazelton, British Columbia, Canada.

1900 Dr. Horace C. Wrinch (physician, agriculturalist), a Methodist Church Missionary Board Physician canoed a nine-week long trip from Port Essington up the Skeena River to Hazelton. He came with his Deaconess wife, a graduate nurse, to practice medicine. He established in Kispiox using a log house as office, dispensary and operating room.

1903 Hazelton Hospital constructed. (Being a crossroads, this location offered a fuller service to all the people of the district).

1904 "Hazelton Hospital" officially opened with 20 beds. A training school for nurses was founded which lasted until 1932.

1907 Two large balconies forming a 12 foot addition was built which proved ideal for tuberculosis patients.

1910 Dr. Horace C. Wrinch ordained.

1914 First X-ray machine installed (cost - $5,000).

1924 Dr. Wrinch was voted into the B.C. Legislature as the Liberal member for Skeena.

1928 Dr. Wrinch as M.L.A. introduced the "Health Insurance Bill".

1930 Second "Hazelton Hospital" opened.

1931 At the world's hospital convention the "Hazelton Hospital" was chosen one of the ten best hospitals in Canada.

1936 Dr. Wrinch retired-

(over 70 years old).

1939 Dr. Wrinch died.

1940 Hospital renamed "WRINCH MEMORIAL HOSPITAL".

1971 The hospital first accredited by the Canadian Council on Hospital Accreditation and which it has since maintained.

1977 The present "Wrinch Memorial Hospital" officially opened.

CHAPTER 6

Alice Jane Breckon Wrinch, 1869-1923: Wife of Pioneer Doctor Harold Cooper Wrinch

The Wrinch Family, 1908,
still to come: Arthur and Harold.
Courtesy of Jessie Gould.

In the cemetery of Old Hazelton is an imposing gravestone standing above a plot overlooking the junction of the Bulkley and Skeena Rivers and the valley of the Skeena, stretching westward to the Seven Sisters Mountains 60 miles away. To the left, Mount Rochier de Boule towers at 7,000 feet, and to the right the high alpine meadows of the Omineca range rise to 6,000 feet. Marking the grave is a vertical granite stone reading: "Alice Jane Breckon, dearly beloved wife of Horace Cooper Wrinch."

This does not tell us the story of this remarkable woman—a deaconess of the Methodist Church, a teacher, a nurse, and, finally, the wife and helpmate of the famous Dr Wrinch. She was born in

1869 in a rural Ontario community and, after completing teachers' training, taught school in a farming settlement near Belleview, Ontario. There she met an earnest young farmer, Horace Cooper Wrinch. The two fell in love and made a joint decision to spend their lives in service to their Lord in the missionary field.

First Horace Wrinch finished his training at the agricultural college in Belleview and then entered medicine at the University of Toronto, where he graduated as a gold medallist. During this time Alice Breckon prepared herself for the missionary field, graduating from a regular nurses' training course. In 1899 they were married and made their way across the continent by CP Rail and, eventually, to Port Essington.

The following spring, in 1900, the Wrinches decided to establish a medical mission at the Native village of Kispiox, some 200 miles up the Skeena River. They decided to take a Native dugout canoe, rather than the sternwheeler that made regular trips to Hazelton, and undertook a nine-week honeymoon voyage up the river (see Chapter 5). Fittingly, their first child, a son, Leonard, was conceived on this journey.

Their mission was established at Kispiox, some 10 miles up the river from Hazelton. Mrs Wrinch assisted with a number of surgeries and often dispensed anaesthetic. When Dr Wrinch was away on house calls, sometimes necessitating two-to-three-day absences, Mrs Wrinch visited the Native women, teaching them how to care for their children and also how to make comfortable clothing for their families.

Even by today's standards Alice would have been considered an elderly first-time mother when Leonard was born in 1901. The birth of Leonard was followed at one-to-two-year intervals by the births of four more children. The Wrinch home was always open to visitors, and a bountiful table was always maintained under the capable management of Mrs Wrinch. The menu featured vegetables from their large garden, fresh fish, milk and dairy products from the hospital dairy, and wild game.

Mrs Wrinch was always described as a gentle and loving person who maintained a gentler kind of discipline than did her husband; that is, she relied on persuasion and reasoning rather than firm commands. In spite of her heavy workload in the home, Mrs Wrinch managed to be active in community affairs and, in 1912, was president of the hospital auxiliary. It is noted that, in a fund-raising drive, she contributed 50 pounds of sugar to be auctioned. With the 1904 establishment of a nursing school in Hazelton, her duties in the hospital were less rigorous. She did, however, attend house calls with Dr Wrinch, and, in the great flu epidemic of 1919, on occasion the two of them could be found late at night wrapped in robes, fast asleep in a horse-drawn cutter.

In that same year Mrs Wrinch became aware of the first signs of a four-year illness. She died in 1923 from cancer. The monument to her life is not found on granite but in improved health for the people of Hazelton, in the modern hospital and medical facilities, and in the life of her husband, Dr Wrinch. It is also to be found in the lives of her children—a medical doctor, a pharmacist, a businessman, a nurse, and, finally, a humanitarian who became a brigadier-general with the Red Cross Worldwide Service. All of this stands as a tribute to this wonderful woman.

CHAPTER **7**

Quesnel and Its 40-Year Love Affair with Dr Paddy Baker

Gerald Rumsey "Paddy" Baker.
Courtesy of Gertrude Fraser.

Why? This is the question. For 40 years there existed a romance between Dr Baker and the city of Quesnel. The hospital is named after him, as are the extended care facility and a school; everywhere there are indications of the affection and respect in which this great man was held.

The association between Baker and Quesnel came about in a rather unusual way. In January 1912 Dr Baker stepped out of the four-horse sleigh that had brought him from the train terminal at Ashcroft, over the Old Cariboo Highway, to Quesnel. Somewhat stiff from the long journey and the cold (it was 43 degrees Fahrenheit below zero), he responded warmly to the greetings of several citizens who met him at the terminal. Dr Baker was told that a sick man lay at the hospital and that "as soon as you can, [he] would like you to come up to see him."

The man turned out to be Fred Brown, a prospector who, in fortifying himself against the bitter cold, had in true Cariboo fashion overdone the job. When he returned to an unheated log cabin he neglected to put on a fire and to take off his shoes. Next morning both his feet were frozen and, when gangrene set in, amputation seemed likely.

Dr Baker handed his suitcases to helping hands, made his way up to the hospital, assessed the situation, and, under open-drop anaesthetic and with light from oil lamps, amputated both of the unfortunate Mr Brown's feet. No doubt he kept in mind the axiom, "For burns amputate high, for frostbite amputate low." At any rate, Mr Brown survived, recovered, and, with prostheses, made his way about the town in a sprightly fashion for the next twelve years. He received much credit for being the means of enticing the doctor to Quesnel.

The physician/surgeon who descended from the sleigh that cold day in January did not appear by chance. Surgeons are born, not made, and no amount of training will ever make a good surgeon if he or she is not already gifted. Gerald Rumsey Baker was born with skilled hands; a keen, decisive mind; and good judgement. Given this, his energy and application then propelled him to excellence.

G.R. Baker was born in Wiltshire, England, in 1873 to Ernest and Mary Baker, who were of Irish stock. His record in public school in England is unknown, but, subsequently disavowing the pastoral life, he elected to go in for a degree in medicine. During his time in university he impressed his professors with his athletic ability—an ability quite necessary to the academic advancement of an Irish lad at that time. By the time he had passed out of medical school he had caught the dean's eye. In those times appointments to good teaching hospitals were not the result of a student's application. The old boys' network was in full operation, and Baker's entrance to St Bartholomew's Hospital likely came about as follows:

"Ring, ring, ring." Sir Henry Butlin picked up the phone. "Sir Henry here."

"Is that you, Henry? It's Reginald over in Trinity."

"Reginald, delighted to hear from you. How are things down in the county?"

"Oh, about as usual. The locals get awkward, but we cope. The reason I called you is that I just passed out a lad who is rather keen, and I thought you might want to have a look at him at Bart's."

"Oh, keen you say? Stout lad, good, respectable family, right religion, and all that?"

"Yes, sturdy lad, good mind, and shows energy. A bit of an unusual prospect."

"Well Reggie, it sounds interesting. Could it be that this boy has some athletic ability?"

"Henry, I would say he's a smart lad. He's a forward in the rugby squad, and they say that he is ferocious in his position. He's also a boxing champion and a cricket whiz."

"It does sound like this lad bears looking into. Why don't we bring him up to Bart's for a time and see how he makes out?"

"Henry, I'm really pleased that you'll take this lad. His name, by the way, is Gerald Rumsey Baker."

And so it was that Gerald Rumsey Baker, age 21, made his way to St Bartholomew's Hospital in London (commonly called "Bart's"). It is the oldest teaching hospital in London, with a history going back over 800 years.

When G.R. Baker arrived, a new graduate from Trinity, one can be sure that he was not greeted with flags flying and bands playing. He was new and at the bottom of the ladder. Dr John Dufton, later a teaching fellow at Bart's, recounts that the great consultants arrived in frock coats three times a week and that in the hospital's teaching rounds there was a traditional pecking order: consultants, teaching fellows, registrars and senior housemen, and then housemen. It was in the latter group that G.R. Baker found himself. His excellence in football and boxing gained him some notoriety, but for the first year he had to be content to learn the medical history of the patients, sharpen his diagnostic skills, and perhaps assist in minor operative procedures. He also had the opportunity to observe the great surgeons in action. Teaching fellows and registrars commonly availed themselves of the assistance of the lowly housemen, and, as the latter gained experience, they were assigned minor surgical procedures.

In his second year at Bart's the keen, young G.R. Baker advanced to more responsible work, assisting the consultants and following up surgery. As a senior houseman, procedures such as appendectomies and minor gynaecological and obstetrical procedures fell into Baker's sphere of action. At the same time there was ample opportunity for him to sharpen his diagnostic skills and to compare his conclusions with those of Sir Thomas Langton and Sir Henry Butlin (re: surgery) and with those of Sir Thomas Brunton (re: medicine)—all great men in the medical world. One can be sure that

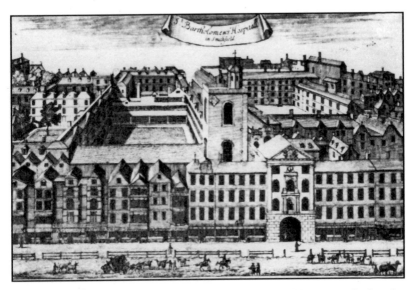

In the 18th century rendering of Bart's the Henry VIII gateway (right of centre) is surrounded by structure. Below it stands alone 200 years later.

his skill at boxing and rugby caught the attention of the consultants and hastened his progress.

At the end of two years in a major British teaching hospital Baker's career in surgery in the British Isles effectively came to an end. While he had his MRCS, there was no opportunity for advancement in the hospital. Consultant posts did not open up either in England or in

Ireland. His only options were either to take a general practitioner post in the country or to emigrate.

For an energetic, skilled young doctor there was actually only one choice, and that was to leave the British Isles. North America, with its large population and wide-open spaces, was his obvious choice, and it was there that he went in 1896. He was an armed guard and medical officer for Wells Fargo in the western United States, practised briefly in the Yukon and Alaska, and finally settled into an assistant position under surgeon Dr Jones in St Joseph's Hospital in Victoria. He was later to say that he learned more under Dr Jones than he had learned in his two years at St Bartholomew's. In 1897 he was registered as physician No. 210 with the College of Physicians and Surgeons of British Columbia.

In 1912, while working with Dr Jones at St. Joseph's, Baker received an opportunity to test his skills in the central interior of British Columbia. An entreaty

G.R. Baker
as Wells Fargo
Medical Officer
Arizona, C. 1900.
Courtesy of Quesnel
and District Museum.

came through to Dr Jones for help with a certain Mr Brown of Quesnel. This was an opportunity that the adventurous Dr Baker could not resist. He shot off to Ashcroft on the train with his medical bag and instruments; caught the horse-drawn stagecoach from Ashcroft to Quesnel; and, approximately a week after departing the mild climate of Vancouver, found himself in the midst of a Quesnel winter.

After performing successful surgery on Mr Brown, G.R. Baker and Quesnel stepped back, appraised each other, and fell in love. Each saw unique qualities in the other. For G.R. it was the wide-open country, the rivers, the streams, the forests. No tidy rock-walled fields limited his walking trips, hunting and fishing were just over the next hill, and there were no "Trespassers Will Be Prosecuted" signs, such as were to be found in abundance in the Old Country. The streams were there to be fished, not to be the private preserve of some gentleman. The geese flew each fall, as did the ducks before them; grouse and partridge abounded; and deer and moose were to be found within a mile or two of the city. To an outdoor-minded person like G.R. Baker this was the closest to heaven that Earth afforded.

In addition, here he could practise his diagnostic and surgical skills. The whole medical world of Quesnel revolved around his personality and skill. About him in the hospital were efficient, clever, enthusiastic nurses, and, as respect and confidence in him increased, so did their abilities to communicate with and to assist him.

Quesnel, with the brash confidence of Interior communities, evaluated G.R. Baker, seeing in him a mature, experienced doctor, well trained, with advanced degrees in surgery from a first-rate teaching centre. There could be no denying that he was keen and ready to do his best to improve the health of the community. Without reservation Quesnel gave the new doctor a resounding vote of confidence.

Dr Baker found lodgings close to the hospital—a building that was not an imposing structure. It was close to the present hospital, was made of logs, and had eight beds. The operating room was in a pantry located close to the kitchen—a fortuitous circumstance, as that is were instruments were sterilized. It was said that the lower legs of the unfortunate Mr Brown were incinerated in that kitchen's stove. The resultant sizzling and crackling had put the nurses off their coffee for weeks.

For surgery, two good anaesthetics were available: ether, which was reasonably safe and very effective, and chloroform, which was very effective but not very safe. Both were given by drop on a mask, providing deep anaesthesia for abdominal operations. Nitrous oxide was used less often than were either ether or chloroform but, interestingly enough, is still in widespread use.

Dr Alex Holley, a fellowship surgeon still residing in Quesnel, observed that G.R. Baker never tired. *He never tired.* He was always vibrant, full of energy, and outgoing. He had talent and style. He was good with his hands, and he was fast. He had few post-operative infection problems; likely his skin carried no infection-causing bacteria. This is important, as some surgeons do carry bacteria on their skin, and this is bad news for their patients who may, as a consequence, suffer post-operative infections.

The nurses found that Dr Baker's confident, cheerful manner immediately made patients feel better. Just by walking through a room he gave patients a boost. His, "You've got a bit of trouble, Mac,

Dr Baker with Matron G. Watt.
Courtesy of Quesnel and District Museum.

but you'll be better soon," did more to boost morale and hasten healing than did any medicine. According to former hospital matron Gertrude Watt Fraser: "He was a great guy, loved so much by everyone and wonderful to work with. His very presence made patients feel better."

It must be remembered that, for the most part, Dr Baker practised medicine in the era before blood transfusions and antibiotics. He performed hundreds of surgeries, gall bladder removals, stomach resections, major resections of cancerous bowels and rectums, prostate surgery, hysterectomies, and Caesarean sections. He had his own technique for evacuating cranial blood clots (see Chapter 27). Even in this era of few effective medications, he rarely lost a patient. When he did, he would go to his farm to mourn for a few days and then return to his duties.

In those days one of the most terrifying situations was that of a young mother hemorrhaging from a misplaced afterbirth or from an afterbirth that had come loose from the wall of the uterus. Here blood loss often exceeded six pints, and there were no blood transfusions. G.R. Baker realized that blood loss must be stopped quickly. Under open-drop anaesthesia, three incisions of his scalpel delivered a crying infant to its crib. With his left hand firmly encircling the lower segment of the uterus, the afterbirth was delivered and blood loss controlled. The right hand placed sutures, one after the other, in the wall of the uterus. At the conclusion of this five-minute procedure the abdominal cavity was washed out with saline solution and then filled with two or three more litres of it. Finally the uterine wall was closed. The whole operation lasted perhaps 15 minutes.

Somewhere during his years of training Dr Baker married. Little is known of this union except that it did not last. On his taking up

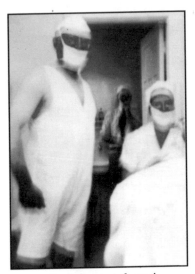

Dr Baker in informal
operating-room attire.
Courtesy of Gertrude Watt Fraser

residence in Quesnel he met, wooed, and, in 1915, married a lovely young woman named Nellie English. Nellie was used to the frontier life, having been raised in the Chilcotin area of central British Columbia (Doc English Lake in the Chilcotin is named after her father). She brought to the union a child (also named Nellie) from a previous marriage, and this young girl's brightness cheered the Baker home. Dr Baker himself had no known children.

Mrs Nellie Baker, nee English, was much loved in Quesnel and frequently drove Dr Baker in a buggy from one house call to the next or to the hospital. In emergencies she summoned the doctor with three shots from a rifle.

Dr Baker, now called "Paddy" because of his Irish background, had an easy, friendly relationship with the hospital personnel, from the janitor to the floor sweeper and on up. New nurses were sometimes disconcerted by his scrubbing for surgery in his underwear. In spite of this eccentricity, his colleagues thought highly of his medical acumen and surgical skill. And to be sure, he did not neglect his postgraduate education, taking trips to attend courses in Vancouver, Chicago, and New York. He was one of the first to use prophylactic sulpha in high-risk surgical operations, and he generally kept abreast of advances in medicine.

Dr Baker once had an experience with a White Russian who made his living trading with the Natives in the Chilcotin. His name was Paul Krestiniuk, and he came to the hospital in Quesnel with symptoms typically associated with acute appendicitis. Dr Baker examined him and told him that he had appendicitis and that his appendix should be removed, particularly as Krestiniuk was often far from medical care. The man was admitted to hospital, but next morning when Dr Baker came around to perform the operation, he had disappeared from the hospital

Dr Alex Holley relates the story as told to him by Paul:

> *"That night I see that nurse go by with a tray full of tools." I say to her, "What for those tools you Have?" She say, "Those are for your operation in the morning." I tell to her, "You get me my clothes." She say, "No, I can't do that." So I say, "OK, you tell me where they are and I get them myself." Anyway he found his clothes and took off from the hospital. He went down to Fraser's barn where he had his four-horse freight team and sleigh, hitched up and took off in the dark for his trading post at Nazko, seventy miles away. He said to me, "You know how I cure'em up those appendix? Olive oil and turpentine! I drink'em that olive oil and I rub my belly with turpentine. I rub and I rub and I rub, and pretty soon my belly pain, she start to feel a little better. And that's how I cure 'em up."*

Far from being offended, Dr Baker roared with laughter and said that he must lay in some of that turpentine and olive oil. Another story concerns an importunate local character who came into Dr Baker's office complaining of a sore jaw, likely an arthritic condition of the T.M. (Temporo-Mandibular) joint. Dr Baker, somewhat impatient because he had an emergency to attend to at the hospital, tried to delay the man and get away from the office. The man finally seized Dr Baker's coat, and informed him that he could not go until he had examined his jaw. Dr Baker, now thoroughly exasperated, hauled back and hit him a mighty blow on the jaw, said, "Take that, you rascal!" and then made his way out the door. As he left the office, the man felt his jaw and, in amazement, exclaimed, "Doc, you did it! You cured me! My jaw is all better!" Dr Baker, looking back, shouted, "That'll be five dollars; pay the nurse," and went on to his emergency call. Throughout the flu epidemic of 1919 and the years of the Depression, Dr Baker made his rounds. Day and night, he was always available. Everywhere patients recovered, and this encouraged others to heal as well.

This is not to say that Dr Baker was without fault. He was known to be somewhat aggressive and was not above a good old Irish brouhaha if the situation demanded it. On one occasion he found a patient holding a knife to the matron's neck. In short order he disarmed the man and subdued him. He received recognition from the Australian government for apprehending a dubious and

A rare photo of Dr. Baker, assisted by Dr. Oliver, in action at Quesnel Hospital in 1938.

aggressive character wanted for murder. As is true of many of the frontier doctors, who were always extended to the limit, he was known to take a drink. But he was also known to refuse a drink, although some of the old-timers have trouble remembering the latter occasions. Even so, there is certainly no evidence, in spite of his Irish background, that drink was a significant factor in Dr Baker's life.

Alice Lindstrom of Watsonville, California, a former resident of the Cariboo, relates the story of Dr Baker and his famed saskatoon-berry wine. A certain English remittance man, Race Horse Johnson of 141 Mile House, had a weakness for drink and, over the Christmas season (which he spent with the Bakers), went through most of G.R.s saskatoon-berry wine. The upshot was that Johnson and Baker, both lovers of horseflesh, differed on the merits of their respective horses. Staging a horse race was the way to resolve the argument. The only problem was that the temperature outside was minus 40 degrees Fahrenheit and there were two feet of snow on the ground. Obviously, the race was never run. Nonetheless Race Horse Johnson got into trouble and was asked to leave town after pounding on the liquor store door, demanding that the store open up. Dr Baker persuaded Alice Lindstrom to chauffeur him back to 141 Mile House and placated the local authorities.

Initially, a team and buggy was used to make house calls. Later, Dr Baker acquired a Ford sedan and, following that, a pick-up. He was never knowledgeable about motorcars and usually drove about in low gear. When he stopped, as often as not it was in the middle of the street to avoid the inconvenience of trying to angle or parallel park. Citizens passing by would notice the doctor's car in the middle of the street, motor running, and would remark that he must be in a hurry that day. If the car seemed to be getting warm, they turned the key to let it cool off.

At other times a canoe was used to transport the doctor from his ranch across the Quesnel River to the hospital site. On one occasion, in answer to a maternity case, Dr Baker pushed the canoe away from the bank on a cold December night (27 degrees Fahrenheit below zero). As he did so the canoe slipped out of his hand and drifted out on the current. Dr Baker splashed out, swam to recapture the canoe, and then climbed in. His wet clothing immediately froze into an armour-like shell. An observer noted his appearance when he reached the far shore and remarked, "Pretty cold night for a dip, ain't it, Doc?" Dr Baker had to admit that it was, but being able to help the poor woman with her baby was worth all the inconvenience.

A story told to me by Dr Al Holley deserves repeating. Alas, he would not vouch for its authenticity. A number of years ago the British Columbia Medical Association held its annual meeting in Quesnel. An item in the entertainment program was a fishing trip to 6 Mile Lake. The doctors departed, and Dr Baker, who was held up at the hospital, arranged to take the ladies to the lake. Slightly late, he picked up the members of the distaff side in his sedan and started for the picnic. On the way he felt a tremendous urge to pass wind. This was suppressed with the utmost effort until he got to the lake. Once there he retired, hoping to relieve himself, but the ladies followed along after him like a bunch of goslings after a goose. Finally, in desperation he took his shotgun and said: "Stand back, ladies, here comes a duck which I'll procure for one of my poor patients in town." A hapless coot came into range, Dr Baker took aim, pulled the trigger, and simultaneously let loose a tremendous fart. There was no joy in Quesnel that day, for the luck of the Irish had deserted him: the gun failed to fire, but Paddy didn't!

Dr Baker experienced the pioneer life to the fullest. He filed on a 160-acre parcel of land across the Quesnel River and did the requisite amount of work to "prove up on it" and to acquire title. Then he filed on another plot. There he built a comfortable log home and appropriate farm outbuildings. He could be seen in chaps, riding gear, and moccasins riding his horse about the farm acres. Patients often paid off their medical bills by building fences, putting up hay, or cutting wood on this farm.

According to Maude Lebourdais, daughter-in-law of the famous Louis Lebourdais, Dr Baker was an expert coyote trapper and, in one season, caught 30 of the wily beasts. The years passed. As Dr Baker grew older, his love for hunting and the countryside did not diminish. He had a remarkable facility for remembering things that occurred in nature. For example, miles away from town he would look at a tree and remark that, 15 years before, he had seen a squirrel under it.

Dr Baker, North Star Ranch,
his ranch home and horse.
Courtesy of Quesnel
and District Museum.

His annual hunting expeditions to
the Chilcotin were in the company of
Charlie Docherty, the Johnsons, and
other old friends. Each fall he went
to the famous Australian Ranch,
twenty miles south of Quesnel, to bag
geese. Here hundreds of acres of
grain and hayland provided ideal locations for hunting blinds. Rarely
was a hunt unsuccessful. On his house calls he carried a famous
double-barrelled gun mounted with a 12-gauge barrel on one side
and a .57 black powder barrel on the other. "For," as he asserted, "if
I see a grouse I can bag him with a 12-gauge, and if I see a bear, I can
down him with the .57." There wasn't much doubt that he could,
since the .57 fired a one-ounce slug. The .57 Snider was a beautiful
hand-tooled gun from England, and the shotgun was an L.C. Smith
12-gauge; he was an expert marksman with either.

Dr Baker was a fisherman and an expert at tying flies. He could
often be found some miles away from Quesnel fishing the streams
or Bouchie Lake with his home-tied flies, often with considerable
success. His fishing may have led to marital problems, for in later
years he was accompanied by a young nurse from the hospital. This
liaison likely began at Barkerville Hospital, where the young nurse
cared for a single patient. Dr Baker spent a few days at the hospital.

This Florence Lindsay painting of Dr. Baker was a runner up in a 1956 contest held by the North Quesnel Women's Institute. The local artist lost out to a mural by Peter Hopkinson that has now decorated the G.R. Baker Memorial Hospital for over forty years. The Lindsay painting is now owned by Maude LeBourdais. Courtesy of Branwen Patenaude.

The patient was discharged, and Doctor Baker's relationship with the nurse intensified.

Doctors' wives are under a certain disadvantage. This is particularly true when their husbands are busy practitioners. Doctors are often at the hospital or involved with patients for 17 hours a day; they come home exhausted and ill-tempered, and meaningful communication with their wives is limited in the extreme. Nurses are respectable young women, often not highly sophisticated, sometimes quite naive. Because of their shift work, they have limited opportunities to meet eligible young men, and the presence of a lively, educated world traveller can be very fascinating. So it was with nurse Helene: she was dazzled, then bedazzled, then bewitched. In a small city like Quesnel nothing goes unnoticed: rumours flew, tongues waggled, and gossip rolled. Nellie put up with this for as long as possible, but when she found G.R. and Helene in a compromising situation she pulled the pin and removed her husband from the family home. She remained on the North Star Ranch through the years, as did her daughter after her. Dr Baker eventually married Helene and lived in town.

Weak men are weak because of their follies; great men are great in spite of their follies. The town was taken aback, because Nellie Baker was much loved, but Dr Baker's reputation suffered only mildly, since it was recognized that he was, after all, only human. It was Helene who took the brunt of the criticism: she was never fully accepted in the community and left after Dr Baker's death.

It is noteworthy that to attain fame one need not conquer the world but only endure steadfastly and surely. Dr Baker had the love and respect of the whole area around Quesnel to such an extent that, when he was attending the Canadian Medical Association meeting in Edmonton, a committee headed up by Fred Lindsay wrote a letter to the president of the association commending him. We do not have the original letter, but we do have Dr Baker's response to it in a letter held in the Quesnel museum. It gives a clear picture of the humility of the man. The letter, beginning "Dear Fred," was written in 1946.

> *Words can't say how I was touched by the letter you wrote to the Medical Association. The president of the Canadian Medical Association when he had me up and introduced to the people in the room, over 500, said I was to be honoured by the Association, how he wanted to read a letter that had been sent to him, and he read your letter to the finish. He said that in his experience the letter was the nicest gesture ever known to a doctor, and through the doctor to the Medical Association. I had a big lump in my throat, and I could not see very well. Thank John and everyone. (Baker to Lindsay 1946)*

Other honours followed. He was nominated a life member of the College of Physicians and Surgeons of British Columbia, his buggy was mounted on the top of Smith's Hardware Store, new hospitals were named after him, and his name remained a household word in the community that he loved and served for so long.

As he approached his seventieth birthday (actually his eighty-first; the Irish are a bit lax in counting their years), the symptoms of his last illness appeared. He had surgery for cancer, continued through disability and failing health, and finally, in 1952, was told the end was near.

Gertrude Fraser tells of Dr Baker's last hunting trip. She and her husband took him to a familiar hunting spot. He was weak and thin but delighted in this adventure, likely knowing that death was close and that this would be his last hunt. At the end, in almost the same words used by Stonewall Jackson of US Civil War fame (also an Irishman), he said, simply and quietly, "Very well, the end it is. I'll go over the river and rest under the trees."

The *Quesnel Advertiser* of November 26, 1955, said it well: "No mountain is high enough to reach up to the summits to which the doctor has gone." So passed from us a great man, Dr Gerald Rumsey Baker. Amen. Not rich in worldly possessions, in spite of his years of labour (for he gave away so much), but rich in the love and affection of his community. In years of ceaseless toil and stress he had fulfilled the most important commandment: "Love thy neighbour as thyself."

CHAPTER 8

Mrs Nellie Baker, Wife Of Gerald Rumsey Baker

Mrs Nellie Baker.
Courtesy of Gertrude Watt Fraser.

An account of the helpmates of frontier doctors would not be complete without a mention of Nellie English Baker. She should have been the perfect wife for an enthusiastic, outdoor-loving man like Gerald Rumsey Baker. She was raised in the Chilcotin, near Riske Creek, the daughter of a rancher who loved race horses and who was noted for his ability to treat animals—an ability that earned him the nickname "Doc English." His daughter Nellie was at home riding a saddle horse or driving a team and buggy, and she knew how to handle firearms.

Nellie English was likely named after Nellie Hance, a much-loved pioneer woman of the Chilcotin, and it is likely that her daughter, also named Nellie, was so named in honour of this respected person, who in 1887, came to the Chilcotin from Vancouver on horseback, a seventeen-year-old bride. Nellie English was to spend much time with the Hance family as a child and young woman.

Nellie Sr described her life in the Chilcotin, remembering that she was at home working around livestock and helping the cowboys round up cattle. At an early age she was a beauty: full-figured, a woman who caught men's eyes whether she was riding a horse or dressed for a dance or party. At age 18 she married and moved to Dragon Lake near Quesnel. Unfortunately, her first husband died from tuberculosis, leaving a young widow with a small child.

Paddy Baker could not fail to notice this attractive young widow. His first marriage had ended several years before, and three years after his arrival in Quesnel he and Nellie were married and settled into a comfortable frontier doctor's life.

Nellie, not having had any nursing experience, undertook a training course under a nurse/anaesthetist at St Paul's Hospital and was able to accompany Dr Baker to out-of-town calls for patients requiring surgery. By the light of kerosene lamps she gave open-drop ether for many operations that took place in miners' or trappers' cabins, tents, hotel rooms, and even bars. This type of anaesthetic poses a considerable risk of explosion or fire, but apparently Nellie was quite successful. Certainly Dr Baker voiced no complaints about her ability to handle it.

Apparently during one of her early operations she fainted and fell to the cabin's floor. Dr Baker, scrubbed and ready for surgery, still showed his tender feelings for his wife, the anaesthetist, by rolling her over and over with his foot towards the open door, where the fresh air soon revived her.

Nellie was an excellent horsewoman and drove Dr Baker from house call to house call in their buggy, handling the horses with an expertise that was the pride of the small city. She was active in civic affairs, hospital committees, and fund-raising drives for worthwhile and charitable causes. The Bakers' home was a comfortable log dwelling on flat land across the Quesnel River from Quesnel itself. Nellie was a noted housekeeper, hostess, and cook. She was also renowned for her home-made wine, usually utilizing the saskatoon berries that grew on their farm.

Why then, after twenty years of marriage, did Dr Baker abandon her and transfer his affections from the gracious, attractive Nellie to a nurse 25 years his junior, who possessed few social skills and little grace? This was a puzzle to the whole community, but the answer goes back as far as human history. Why did David abandon all principle and seduce Bathsheba? Why did Napoleon leave Josephine, John F. Kennedy betray Jacqueline? The answer is that men with power covet women, just as do dominant males in the animal kingdom.

The now single Nellie Baker continued in the love and affection of the whole community. Gerald Rumsey's stature was somewhat diminished because of this liaison, while Helene, his new interest, was actively disliked and avoided. Gerald was cast from the family home and farm to live in a house in Quesnel. His new marriage, while legal, was hardly recognized, and Nellie was generally regarded as the true Mrs Baker. She continued to live in the comfortable farm home until her death, and Dr Al Holley tells me that, at age 70, she was still a strikingly beautiful woman.

Gerald Rumsey seems to have had a less than ideal third marriage. Helene was not the type to go riding out into the wilds to summon him with rifle shots for emergency patients. She was not the type to drive him from place to place on house calls. And she had limited social skills. Perhaps her performance in bed made up for all these deficiencies, but one has to be a little sceptical. There is a poem that goes:

> *When I was young and in my prime*
> *I used to want it all the time,*
> *But now I'm old and getting grey,*
> *I only want it twice a day.*

Perhaps Dr Baker was such a man, but there is reason to suspect that, in his later years, his nubile young bedmate lost her attraction and he regretted his separation from the beautiful and gracious Nellie English Baker—a true frontier woman, loved and respected by everyone in the Quesnel area.

CHAPTER 9

The Cross And The Scalpel

Father Nicholas Coccola, OMI, Priest, Missionary,
Surgeon, Dentist, Midwife, School Administrator

New settlers in the Nechako Valley at the turn of the century had little need for medicine or doctors, as most were young and healthy. The rare serious accident victim of gunshot, farming, or logging mishaps either lived or died under whatever rudimentary care available. However, sickness did occur, and an excerpt from *Vanderhoof: The Town That Wouldn't Wait* by the Nechako Historical Society describes the treatment for common ailments. Margaret Brain tells us that infected wounds were treated with carbolic antiseptic. Cuts were dusted prophylactically with Iodiform, a strong-smelling yellow powder. Everyone kept a bottle of rum or whisky strictly for medicinal purposes. Jamaica Ginger mixed in sweetened hot water relieved abdominal cramps and stomach ache and, likely, menstrual cramps.

Colleen Dovell remembers that her mother cured all ills with Dr Thomas's Electric Oil. Although this is now marked as poison, at that time two drops of the oil on sugar were considered to be good for fevers, colds, and upset stomachs. Colleen's father, who lived to the age of 85, said it was the only medicine he ever took. The horses got it, the cows got it, and the humans got it. Another pioneer remembers that placing warm raw onions on her child's chest and putting a bandage around his nose was a sure method of shaking off the "croup."

Velma Johnson recalls that bromo and quinine were used as cold treatments and that mustard plasters were used to relieve bronchial congestion. Sal volatile could be bought, and it was claimed that it could bring a person out of a faint. Parents used steam then, as now, for respiratory distress. They gave their children ipecac if it was necessary to make them vomit.

In the Fort George area during this time of no nurses and doctors, there was a makeshift hospital (described as a large tent) where new mothers took their babies, along with sacks of potatoes, to bed to

Father Coccola, c. 1910.
Courtesy of Fraser Fort George Regional Museum.

keep them from freezing. Our first knowledge of the use of modern medicine in the Fort George area occurs with the arrival of Father Nicholas Coccola in 1905. The late Kay Cronin, author of *Cross in the Wilderness,* states: "Father Coccola was a Corsican, ...the same fireball personalities."

According to Cronin, prior to coming to north-central BC, Coccola was in the Kamloops region. Here, in 1881, the English-speaking settlers were spellbound by eloquent sermons delivered with a strong Corsican accent. Young Native people were overjoyed that they could understand the new missionary (who likely spole Chinook jargon) and that he could join them in horseback riding. Father Coccola was an excellent rider and had only to mention that he liked a particular horse before the Natives would straightway present it to him.

Father Coccola arrived in the Fort George area in 1905 and served north-central BC for nearly forty years. According to Reverend F.E. Runnalls, Father Coccola had some medical training and was in a position to minister to the sick and to help many who were beyond the reach of a medical doctor. He came to be a friend of the White people as well as of the Native people. Runnalls also advises that

Father Nicolas Coccola near Prince George c. 1912.
"We hae meat and we can eat and sae the lord be thank it."
Robert Burns　　　　　　　　　(BCARS F-2964)

Father Coccola visited the Natives regularly at Fort George until 1914, when the village was moved to Shelley. His visits were made twice a year and were outstanding events for the Natives. When word reached the village that he was coming, the Natives gathered on the bank of the river to welcome him. On his arrival he was welcomed with a volley of musket and rifle fire, every Native contributing all the ammunition he had on hand.

Kay Cronin disputes the alleged "fact" that Father Coccola had medical training, but states that from his earliest days as a missionary he was renowned for his work in the field of medicine. While this applied to most of the early missionaries, Father Coccola is the one who, more than any other, is credited with the power of healing.

According to Father Coccola's memoirs, as cited by Cronin, it all began at Kamloops. "The carpenters building the boys' school were first class mechanics," he wrote.

> *I saw the opportunity of making myself useful*
> *and learning the trade, which has been of great help*
> *to me everywhere I went, building houses, schools,*
> *churches and hospitals. All the spare time I had was*

spent with the carpenters or with Brother Surel in his new garden and orchard. One Saturday, wishing to finish a piece of work that the carpenters had left undone, I cut my thumb so badly I did not know if I should say Mass wearing a bandage before the whites. But having some tincture of arnica, I applied it all during the night and in the morning the bleeding had stopped and the wound had closed, though I shall carry the scar to my grave. That gave rise to the rumor that I was a doctor, and from that time Whites and Indians came for medicine. (Coccola in Cronin 1960, 193-94)

So efficient did Father Coccola become in his work as doctor, dentist, surgeon, and midwife that many people presumed he must have had formal training in medicine. This was not so. The only training Father Coccola ever received was that derived through private study and practical experience. Hardly a day passed without his being called upon to treat a fever, pull a tooth, sew a wound, or set a broken bone. For tooth-pulling he used the only anaesthetic available. He would knock the patient senseless with a good blow to the jaw, pull the tooth, then douse him with cold water to bring him around again. For wisdom teeth, which took a little longer, Father Coccola would enlist the aid of four strong men to hold the patient down until the operation was complete (p. 194).

Father Norman Racette, OMI, an elderly Oblate now living in the Texas area and still active in his ministry, recalled how, as a young missionary on one of his latest visits to Prince George, he was called upon to assist Father Coccola in one of his surgical procedures. The patient was an elderly Native woman with an eye problem. The instruments were ready, and both priests had washed their hands. Father Racette was quite concerned about what appeared to be a lack of anaesthetic or anyone to administer it. Upon questioning Father Coccola about this matter, he was reassured that everything had been taken care of. Just prior to starting the surgery, Father Coccola turned quickly and hit the patient on the jaw with an uppercut, which knocked her unconscious. The surgery was then performed and, when the patient awakened, she did not complain so much about a sore eye as she did about a sore jaw.

Kay Cronin tells us that Coccola was gifted in setting fractures. When a man broke a limb, Father Coccola would grab the first thing handy to use as a splint—usually roof or siding shingles, and rip shirts and sheets into ribbons to use as bandages.

In mentioning a few of the countless occasions when he was called upon to act as doctor and surgeon to his flock, Father Coccola was a past master of understatement. One time he was called to a mining camp at Wild Horse Creek. "One of the miners had the frontal bone cut by the blow of an axe," he wrote in his memoirs. "As the brain protruded, I pressed it back, and by antiseptic applications, he was able to return to work after four months." And again: "The customs officer at Fort Steele developed blood poisoning in the right hand. I rendered him assistance, with the result that after six months new flesh covered the bones, and the hand, although a little stiff for a while, became normal." One time he mentions that, "as there were no doctors in the district, I was called day and night by White or Indian in all kinds of accidents and sickness." On another occasion, he recorded simply, "The Hudson's Bay manager sent me one of his employees who had broken his leg. After four weeks he could walk." (p. 195)

Even in later years, when there were more qualified doctors in the province, Father Coccola was still called upon to practise his extra-curriculum profession. Recalling the fatal flu epidemic of 1918, he described his part in it as follows:

> *In October 1918 an epidemic of malignant influenza spread like wild fire through the province taking victims everywhere, especially through the Nechako Valley. For the whole month I had to attend the sick and bury the dead. As they were all more or less attacked and unable to make coffins and dig graves, they were buried in shallow trenches at four and five every morning. The doctor being away, I had to travel day and night for the whites were also dying like the Indians ... A message coming from Stuart Lake that three Sisters and the two Priests were down with the flu, I left at once landing there in the night, and remained there until Priests and Sisters were able to resume work. I found fourteen dead in the village. Trenches were dug and all buried in one day. Others had died in their trapping ground and since nobody was strong enough to bury them they were eaten by dogs. In the end, I had a touch of the sickness,*

but by nose-bleeding I was relieved. I kept on moving,
though it took me two months to be free of dizziness.
(p. 195)

It was not until the worst of the epidemic was over that the local doctor returned to the scene and Father Coccola was able to hang up his stethoscope for a while.

At no time did Father Coccola refuse to give medical aid when it was needed. During his many years of service in the Fraser Lake area, he delivered many Native as well as White babies. In 1918, Mrs Margarita Foote's child, Frances (now Frances Franks of Vanderhoof) was delivered by Father Coccola at the Footes' home just west of the Stellaquo Reserve.

Cronin notes that every once in a while Father Coccola introduced into his memoirs a little of the philosophy of his compatriot, Napoleon Bonaparte. One time he met a minister of a Protestant sect. The clergyman had praised Father Coccola for his work in the Kootenays, then added, "One thing I find strange in your Church is the vow of celibacy. Before I was married I experienced hesitation on the part of the people towards me, but after I was married I was welcome everywhere." To which Father Coccola replied, "You praise me for the work done, yet how could I do it if I was married? I had to be with those sick or dying of typhoid and smallpox. How could I go after that, to my family and bring the germs? It would be cruelty and injustice. Then, you see, one of the two must be neglected—the work, or the family." Warming up to his subject, the fiery Corsican shelved the teachings of the church for a while and turned to the philosophy of his fellow countryman. "Leaving aside St Paul," he continued, "I take the testimony of Napoleon, who had a good knowledge of human nature, and who testified that his best generals were unmarried. The married ones, at the bugle call to march, would hesitate, thinking of their families, but the unmarried would lead their men to victory or death" (p. 198).

Father Coccola's ministry included not only spiritual and medical help but also educational guidance. During the latter part of 1922 he became priest and administrator of the Lejac Residential School. His final years were spent as chaplain at the Smithers Hospital. He passed away on May 1, 1943, at the age of 88 and was buried in the Lejac cemetery near the school that he had worked so hard to build. So ended his long and fruitful career as a healer of mind, body, and soul.

CHAPTER 10

Dr David Brownlee Lazier: A Doctor with Bad Luck

Dr David Brownlee Lazier
could have been rich and famous
but fortune passed him by.
Courtesy of Grace Foote.

Dr Lazier was well known in the central British Columbia area between Prince George and Burns Lake in the years between 1910 and 1930. I first learned about him in an unusual fashion. During a yearly hunting trip southeast of Williams Lake in 1976, I was sitting in the midst of a clump of alder brush when I heard the crackling of branches in the distance and the thud of hooves on hard ground. Since the disturbance was upwind from me, I simply waited for the quarry to approach. The crackling grew louder and there was a sound of trees being rubbed. Suddenly I sniffed the scent of a cigar. It is most unusual for a moose to smoke cigars, and I rightly judged that a hunter was approaching rather than a game animal.

Sure enough, a short time later an elderly individual, mounted on a horse, stopped in front of me and eyed me speculatively. People in the wild can judge quite accurately the wood-wise exposure of another individual. As I observed him, I could see that he was a city person, but the way he slouched in the saddle and, in particular, the position of his gun in the scabbard suggested that he also had a good deal of woods experience. Nonetheless, the fact that he was hunting downwind suggested that he had been separated from this environment for some time. He, on his part, could see that I was used to the woods.

He gave me his name and said he was from Vancouver Island. I asked him where he had gained his experience in the woods. He told me that he had been raised in Fort Fraser and was an old-timer in that area. The reason for his riding a horse was that his legs had troubled him since he had fractured his foot when he was six years old. His doctor at the hamlet of Fort Fraser was an old horse doctor named David Lazier. Because this man had been on a three-day party, a good deal of time elapsed before the boy's fracture could be treated. Lazier was blamed for the poor result. I was quite dubious, since in some institutions no urgency is given to fractures.

David Brownlee Lazier, a native of Ontario, came into the world in 1870 and eventually graduated from Queen's University. He was born to bad luck, his life being a series of misfortunes, tragedies, and missed opportunities. His father was a businessman in southern Ontario, and his family was able to provide him with a university education. He graduated in 1899 and, the following year, he was registrant No. 289 at the College of Physicians and Surgeons of British Columbia.

Little is known of his adventures for the next 10 years. He was married, and the first of his several tragedies was that his wife died at an early age. In 1910, with limited prospects in the Lower Mainland, he made his way up to Soda Creek between Williams Lake and Quesnel, caught the *BX* steamer, and, on a summer day, arrived in South Fort George. He found that there was no registered doctor in the area, although a Corsican priest, Father Coccola, provided some medical care. Dr Lazier felt that he could contribute to the area's medical needs and so set up his practice in South Fort George. He built a three-bed hospital (called Lazier's Hospital), and when, in the flu epidemic of 1912, the number of sick people exceeded this building's capacity, a tent provided overflow space.

In 1912 there was a good deal of activity around the building of the Grand Trunk Pacific Railway from Jasper to Prince Rupert. Ten thousand workman recruited from Europe and across Canada were divided into camps every 18 to 20 miles, and most of these camps had their own physician.

Doctors Richardson and Blakesly provided care for the camps in the Prince George area, but some of their practice fell upon Dr Lazier. Ted Williams tells the story of a Mr Anderson, a foreman on the railway construction crew, who brought an ailing workman to see Dr Lazier. Unfortunately, when the workman (who suffered from a swollen jaw and an aching tooth) arrived, Dr Lazier was in the midst of a loud and merry party near the Island Cache, a marshalling yard for the railway. It was impossible to persuade the doctor to leave the party, and it was several hours before his services could be obtained. Late at night the man was seen in Dr Lazier's kitchen in South Fort George, where he was given a shot of morphine and his tooth was extracted at the doctor's kitchen table. The railway foreman was not overly impressed with his workman having to suffer for five hours before being given medical care.

Dr Lazier delivered Prince George's renowned old-timer, Mr Ted Williams, at home, and this was probably the most dangerous day in Ted's life. Luckily for her, Ted's sister arrived in the world under the care of Dr Carl Ewert, the Williamses having quickly changed doctors as soon as the latter arrived on the scene.

In 1915 Dr Lazier sold his practice to Dr Ewert and enlisted in the army, serving for three years at the rank of captain. He then returned to the central Interior and practised in the Fort Fraser-Fraser Lake-Burns Lake area for the next 10 years. Probably he was active at South Bank across Francois Lake as well, since in 1920 a hospital was established in the home of John Keefe. This building had three beds and, initially, was restricted to female patients. Miss Kennedy, a very competent nurse sent out by the Women's Missionary Society in Toronto, was its capable matron.

It is not clear when Dr Lazier arrived in the Francois Lake area, but it was likely around 1921. He practised there and in Burns Lake for several years. In 1924, Dr Wilson apparently arrived from the missionary society in Toronto, and he and a Mrs Garden set out to move the entire contents of the hospital to Burns Lake. Of course they could not move the building because it belonged to the Francois Lake Hospital Society—a very zealous guardian. This move was further complicated, as a Mrs Newguard (from Grassy Plains) was camped beside the Prosser Point Francois Lake Hospital in the late stages of pregnancy, expecting to deliver at that facility. When the hospital's contents were moved, Mrs Newguard developed complications and required hospitalization. Local members of the hospital society brought in whatever equipment was available, and Dr Lazier himself carried in a stove to heat the hospital for mother and baby.

Mrs Newguard was successfully delivered of a baby girl, and all was well; but bitter feelings lingered between the Francois Lake Hospital Society and Burns Lake for many years. It is not clear whether this was the cause of Dr Lazier moving to Fraser Lake, where a log home, including an office for his medical practice, was built for him. He continued to practise from his home for the next five or six years. It was during this time that my unfortunate hunter suffered a fractured foot and required his treatment.

Dr Lazier's reputation never did improve, and hard luck continued to dog him. His second wife, who might have enhanced his lifestyle, died tragically during childbirth, along with the infant. Dr Lazier's brother, Colonel Lazier, came out from the east and remained with him, as did his nephew, Ted Lazier.

Dr Lazier had an opportunity to become a rich man. In partnership with others he staked a claim on a mining property, but the claim was allowed to lapse. Subsequently Endako Mines, the second largest molybdenum mine in the world, was established on this property. The early claim would have been worth a great fortune had it been maintained.

Tragedy and an unfortunate lifestyle claimed Dr Lazier in 1931. A man whom fame and fortune had missed developed a melancholy that was worsened by substance abuse. The best that can be said of him is that he endured in a harsh land for 21 years. May he rest in peace.

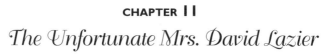

CHAPTER II

The Unfortunate Mrs. David Lazier

Susan Moffitt Lazier
before tragedy struck.
Courtesy of Grace Foote.

Dr David Brownlee Lazier was married twice. His first wife is unknown in the central Interior, as Dr Lazier was a widower when he first came to Prince George in 1910. When he was approximately 53 years of age he married again at Fraser Lake. The second Mrs Lazier was a pleasant, shy English lass, somewhat younger than her husband.

This could have been a period of happiness and contentment, but fate dictated otherwise. Susan Lazier, at age 28, did not have access to all the modern methods of birth control, and soon after their marriage she became pregnant. Looking at her picture I would immediately assess her as high risk for pregnancy. She was an old-looking primipara. And her frame was heavy and her hips straight, which is often indicative of a poor pelvis for delivering an infant. Just from her picture I would have sent her to Edmonton, Vancouver, or the Mayo Clinic. Wherever—just so long she did not spend the last portion of her pregnancy in Fraser Lake.

In early spring she went into labour with three of the local women in attendance, one of whom was a practical midwife with considerable experience delivering babies. After many hours of non-progressive labour, Dr Cuzner was summoned from his cottage at Stella. He assessed the situation and decided that the baby was dead. He dismembered the baby, delivering it in pieces. A morbid Mrs Lazier was then transported to Prince George by train. While earlier it might have been possible to transfer her and her baby to Prince George, this was no longer an option. After 100 agonizing miles she arrived in Prince George in a terminal state.

One can well appreciate the agony this poor woman experienced through her prolonged labour and transfer. The mental anguish of Dr Cuzner, Dr Lazier, and the women who had worked so long and faithfully can only be imagined. It is reported that Dr Cuzner, in shock, lay on the floor and sobbed. Dr Lazier was overwhelmed with grief.

After this tragedy David Lazier could not be comforted. Some months later, in spite of the continued presence of his brother, he, too, passed from the scene, heavily sedated. To this day, Dr and Mrs Lazier and their stillborn child lie together in the Prince George cemetery.

CHAPTER 12

The Beloved Physician, Dr George Cuzner

Dr George Cuzner (far left) overseas during the
First World War, far from peaceful Endako.
Courtesy of George Foote.

He was mild, pleasant, and, in modern terms, somewhat laid back. In some ways he seemed more like a kindly postman than a bulwark of modern medicine in an isolated frontier country. And, indeed, for many years he did manage the post office in Endako Flats near Fort Fraser. When he retired from his practice to go overseas between 1914 and 1918, he assigned the job of postmaster to a neighbour.

His military career, I think, was very traumatic to him. At any rate, he entered the army with the rank of captain, which was consistent with his medical training, and four years later he came out with the same rank. This was certainly modest recognition for a man who had served for this length of time. At the end of this terrible conflict, Captain George Cuzner returned to his rustic life on Stella Flats west of Fraser Lake.

His small cottage on the north side of the Endako River at Stella Flats must have seemed like heaven to a man who had been exposed to four years of horror in the bloody conflict in France. Once home he settled back into a quiet routine, and young people flocked to his cottage for refreshments and a visit with their friend. As far as is known, he was never married, and the reason for his arrival at Stella Flats was not generally known. The school teacher, Kay Morrow, who visited frequently knew the reason but would never divulge it. A colleague in the area, Dr Ed McDonnell, was also kept in the dark. It may have been a medical problem, women problems, financial problems—who knows?

What is known of his previous life is that he had a general practice in Ottawa, left it, and came to a locum practice in Quesnel, British Columbia. Dr Cuzner's introduction to the Fort Fraser area came about in 1910, when he was in Quesnel. A message came through that he would be required for a maternity case in the Vanderhoof area. He made his way across the Fraser River at Quesnel; secured a horse; and, with a sleigh containing hay, provisions, and sleeping cover, made his way up the Blackwater Road. The first night out, according to Dr Al Mooney, Dr Cuzner made up his bed on the sleigh with a mattress of hay. During the night he was awakened by the unusual sensation that his bed was moving. On becoming further awakened, he found that the horses were eating the hay that made up his mattress.

On his arrival in the Vanderhoof area, Dr Cuzner found that the expectant mother, Mrs Snell, was unsure of the date for the arrival of the baby. With true frontier dedication, he remained with the family for the next two months until the baby arrived. He stayed a further month to make sure that lactation was established and that the mother was fit, and then he returned to Quesnel. Impressed with the hospitality of the people in the Fort Fraser-Vanderhoof area, he decided to move there.

Dr Cuzner graduated from McGill University in 1896 but was never registered in British Columbia. He did not attempt to build up a large practice, but it was known that he would never refuse to see someone in need. Many babies were delivered by Dr. Cuzner. One particularly anguishing time occurred when he was called in late to care for Susan Lazier, wife of his colleague Dr David Lazier. As has been related in Chapter 11, both Mrs Lazier and her baby died.

Dr Cuzner gave up his post office duties in September 1919, and it would seem that he had some secure income. He was never known to send a bill for his services, and he never refused to provide care to anyone. He was described as being about 5 feet 6 inches tall, with a light complexion and a full head of hair (which thinned through the years). Invariably he wore a jacket, dress shirt, and tie. Even in this isolated area he maintained an interest in cultural events, and on an old Edison crank gramophone he played numerous symphonies and operas on the wax 33 1/3 rpm disks. His small cottage became a gathering place for people interested in fine music.

Life assumed a tranquil pattern after Dr Cuzner's four years of hell in France. The seasons came and went beside the smooth, slow-moving Endako River: he tended his flowers and his garden, gave his services when required, and enjoyed many years of a peaceful life.

In 1951 he developed symptoms of prostate cancer, and after surgery and treatment in St Paul's Hospital in Vancouver came back to spend his last days in the Fort Fraser area that he loved so much. Vesta Philpott relates that in his last weeks he foresaw that he might be crippled by a stroke, and so he laid out food and water on the cottage floor. And indeed just such an event occurred. Dr McDonnell, checking on Dr Cuzner's cabin, found him stricken and lying on the floor. He had been there five days.

Dr Cuzner's medical bag and memorabilia are preserved in the Vanderhoof museum—a fitting tribute to a physician who was much loved and to whom the area owed so much.

CHAPTER 13

Construction Camp Doctors of North-Central BC

One of the great construction enterprises of the twentieth century was the building of the Grand Trunk Pacific Railway. Initial surveys of the route from Lucerne near Jasper to Prince Rupert were begun in 1908. In 1910 actual construction was begun, with simultaneous clearings of rights of way at Lucerne in the east and at Prince Rupert in the west. Since only very primitive implements were used (i.e., pick and shovel, axe, wheelbarrow, and horse-drawn scrapers), construction was very labour intensive. Ten thousand men were employed at one time. They were drawn from Eastern Canada and Western Europe; and large numbers came from Poland, the Ukraine, and Russia. Foley, Welch, and Stewart were the prime contractors. Since government financing was guaranteed if the line were to be finished in 1914, the energetic Foley journeyed to Eastern Europe to recruit workers when not enough enlisted from Canada and Western Europe.

The men were described as young, strong, and healthy. One dollar a month was withheld from their salary of three dollars per day to

In 1914 the first Grand Trunk train moves westward using the new Shoo Fly Bridge to cross the Nechako River near Fort Fraser.
Courtesy of Lenore Rudland.

Grand Trunk Pacific Hospital, 1912, Prince George.
Courtesy of Fraser Fort George Regional Museum (FFGRM).

cover medical and hospital care. Major tent and log construction camps accommodating 1,000 to 2,000 men were established, starting at Summit near present-day Lucerne and extending to Hazelton. These were located at 100-mile intervals and each had a crude log hospital with one or two attending physicians and a reasonable stock of surgical instruments. Appendectomies could be performed, lacerations sutured, and fractures set. Basic drug formularies were maintained with supplies distributed to the Prince George area by Coles Pharmaceutical, located in Vancouver. These were delivered to the camps by George Williams, the father of the late Ted Williams, a local Prince George historian. (It is to Ted Williams that I am indebted for much of this material, which was obtained by interview, the final one occurring on December 18, 1995, just two weeks prior to his untimely passing on December 31.) There did not seem to be a problem recruiting skilled medical help. According to Ted Williams the construction camp doctors had a reputation for being well trained and competent. However, the fact that they were forbidden to care for patients other than construction workers was a source of friction. And it seems that settlers were not officially allowed into the hospitals (although, apparently, there were exceptions to this rule).

The doctors were mainly from Eastern Canada, Ireland, and Britain. According to the College of Physicians and Surgeons of British Columbia most of these people were not registered. Much primary medical care was provided by paramedical people, most of whom were recruited from the police. These people worked at first-aid stations in the satellite camps; provided basic medicines; and travelled up and down the line to oversee sanitation, sewer facilities, and hygiene. Undoubtedly these people were of the greatest benefit to the health of the workers.

Dr Rhycard of McBride, called Mile 90, arrived in 1911 and continued to care for patients until 1916. He was not registered in BC but provided care to both the settlers and the construction workers. He boarded with a family in McBride and used a front room as a consulting office. According to Marian Wheeler's *The Robson Valley Story* he also had access to three hospital beds located in a private home.

Prince George had two prominent doctors, Hugh McSorley and Cecil Swenerton. There were also, for a short time, Doctors Richardson and Blakesly, about whom little is known. They worked at a large construction hospital built in 1912 in a suburb called the Island Cache. A year earlier an interim facility, the Doctor Lazier Hospital or the Fort George Hospital, was built in central Fort George.

Dr Hugh McSorley was born in 1876 and graduated from McGill University in 1900. Little is known of his background, but he was registered as British Columbia's 279th doctor. He arrived in Prince George in 1911 and practised out of the Doctor Lazier Hospital until the Island Cache Hospital was built in 1912.

The flu epidemic of 1912 strained medical facilities to the limit. Two hospital facilities were established in private homes by nurses F.M. Mandrell and a Miss Elliot, and these were utilized by Dr McSorley. Babies were delivered either at home (probably the safest place), in the nurses' facilities, or in the hospital (probably the most dangerous place because of risk of infection and the possibility of meddlesome obstetrics).

Dr Cecil Swenerton, a 1911 graduate of the University of Toronto, was registered in BC in 1911 and arrived in Prince George the same year. He came from a medically talented family in southern Ontario, and the medical tradition is carried on by his nephew, Ken Swenerton, an oncology specialist with the BC Cancer Institute in Vancouver. Ken supplied details of his uncle's medical career. Initially, Cecil practised out of his rented home, making frequent house calls. He also cared for railway construction workers, admitting them to private hospitals.

In 1912, when the Grand Trunk Pacific Hospital was constructed, it served as a central referral centre for more serious cases up and

Dr Cecil Swenerton and office, c. 1914.
Courtesy of FFGRM.

down the line. It repaid a debt to the Prince George area by admitting private patients and maternity cases. Ninety miles west, at Beaumont near Fraser Lake, there was a construction camp. In 1911 a log hospital graced this facility, and working there was a gregarious, six-foot, handsome graduate of the Toronto Medical School. Dr George Ferguson, although not licensed to practice in BC, maintained a solid presence in the community. He is remembered for two events, one of which is recounted by Lenore Rudland in *Fort Fraser (Where the Hells Is That?).*

The first event involves a certain Mr Mitchel, who, while practising hockey, fell and broke his knee cap. Dr Ferguson elected to wire the fractured sesamoid bone. "Preparation was simple, the largest flannelette nightgown available was draped over the patient, instruments were boiled two hours while an operating table was constructed by placing a door over two sawhorses. The incision was made, holes bored in the kneecap and the edges of the fracture approximated with German Silver wire" (Rudland, 1988, 119). The operation was a complete success, except that the druggist on the floor below appeared, demanding that someone come down and clean up the blood and water dripping through his ceiling.

The second event involves one of the greatest disasters in railway history—a disaster that, for the most part, is curiously ignored. A large rock bluff near Burns Lake was obstructing construction. Huge amounts of explosives were placed in "coyote holes" (15-inch holes drilled deep in the bluff). By some misadventure the powder ignited prematurely. Fifteen men on the site and a further 20 men on a small island were killed. Dr Ferguson, paddling a small canoe to obtain a good view, was swept across the lake by a great wave and caught up in the trees. The canoe was smashed and Dr Ferguson was left dangling on a tree branch. The dead were buried on the small island, which, to this day, is referred to as "Deadman's Island" (Turkki, 1973, 27).

Eighty miles further west, a Dr A.H. Wallace worked in a small hospital at Telkwa and also helped at the hospital in Hazelton, where the famous Dr Wrinch served as railway doctor. Dr Wallace was joined in 1920 by a McGill graduate, Dr G.C. Paine. Dr Ross Stone served as the Grand Trunk Pacific doctor in Vanderhoof.

With the completion of the railway just east of Fraser Lake in April 1914, workers were immediately discharged and daily trainloads of them—500 men to a train—were sent eastwards. Foley, Welch, and Stewart, hoping to construct a North-South line from Prince George, established three construction camps between Prince George and Williams Lake at Cottonwood, Quesnel, and Soda Creek, respectively. However, the First World War intervened, and these camps were closed to make way for grimmer work.

For the most part, the construction camp doctors were not registered in BC and, after the completion of the railway, returned to their homes in the east. For the years between 1910 and 1914, however, they were a vital part of the medical work of north-central British Columbia, and their contribution deserves to be recognized.

Logging camps and mines often had resident positions. As early as 1893, Dr James Clarke of Coombes Hospital, Dublin, served the farming and steamship centre of Soda Creek in the Cariboo. The Bullion Mine, forty miles northeast, had a small hospital of four beds and was served by Dr Dundas Herald from the nearby community of Quesnelle Forks between the years 1897 and 1901. Dr C.A. Wilkins came to the Bullion Mine in 1898 and was relieved in 1906 by Dr Cecil Boyd, who later relocated to 150 Mile House. In

Dr George Ferguson (on right).
Courtesy of Lenore Rudland.

1908 Dr Charles Cobbett came here briefly, prior to moving to a more sedate practice in Edmonton. He was registered with the College of Physicians and Surgeons and was an 1890 graduate of the University of Edinburgh. Dr Wilkins returned from time to time, as needed, and was to be associated with the Bullion Mine for almost forty years.

Dr R.H. Scott was resident physician at the Fraser Mills, sixty miles east of Prince George, between 1910 and 1917, before moving to New Westminster. Another sawmill resident physician was Dr Edwin James Lyon, who was employed by the Eagle Lake Sawmill prior to moving west to Prince George.

These physicians, while serving diligently, had little means to alter the course of serious illnesses. For their years of stressful service they received a mere pittance of $1500 a year. It is not surprising that most moved on to larger centres with well-equipped hospitals and a more civilized lifestyle.

CHAPTER 14

The Pioneer Doctor of Vanderhoof: Dr Ross Stone

Dr Ross Stone, McGill, 1913.
Courtesy of Margaret Calvert.

After the construction of the Grand Trunk Pacific Railway it was somewhat easier for the central BC communities to recruit doctors. One of these was Dr Ross Stone, a great man and a great physician. He was a skilled doctor, faithful to his calling, and, through his work and inspiration, he shaped the future of the community. The ancient Greeks said that the whole country stands as a testimony to a great man. To this day the hospital, the community health service, the school sports programs, and immunization programs for children maintain the memory of Ross Stone's life and work. Many people in the Vanderhoof area carry the name Ross or Stone, marking the hundreds of nights that he dealt with maternity cases, often returning in the light of early morning, completely exhausted but filled with the joy of having played a part in the advent of a new life. Dr Stone delivered over 2,000 babies.

In responding to a call from Fort Fraser some 20 miles to the west, Dr Stone availed himself of a unique method of transportation. The roads were impassable and the only available transport was a hand car on the Grand Trunk Pacific Railway. The two Silver brothers volunteered to hand-pump the scooter along the tracks on a cold evening in early winter. Dr Stone, with his medical bag and delivery pack, wound himself around the vertical stand through which the locomotion was obtained. The venture proved successful and a healthy baby was delivered. It was fortunate that he was a gold medalist in obstetrics because every obstetric complication possible fell under his care. The only maternity case that he lost was one of severe eclampsia, and to this day, with all our medications, this type of loss still occurs.

Ross Stone's daughter, Margaret Calvert, told me that the fees raised from maternity cases went to her mother to clothe her and her two sisters and to purchase a few little extras for the home. Unfortunately, in pioneer communities money was extremely scarce, and payment was often made in kind; that is, in meat, vegetables, or hay. Dr Stone's wife was heard to exclaim that a mother couldn't clothe three growing daughters in a stack of hay.

Pioneer doctors did not become rich, for they cared for people who often did not have money. Some of the copies of Dr Stone's accounts came into my possession, and, on reviewing them, I could determine certain characteristics of his practice. An office visit was $2.50 and a delivery was $20. I also noted that one week's billing amounted to $203 and that a second week's amounted to $291. This represented a considerable sum of money in those early days, but one must reckon that much of it was probably never paid.

Dr Stone practised from an office in a log house built on 40 acres alongside the meandering, slow-moving Nechako River. Much of his time was involved with making house calls, and these might be a block or 50 miles away. They might involve a saddle-horse journey; transport in his democrat buggy north towards Fort St James, south to Stoney Creek, and beyond; a boat journey up and down the Nechako River; or, if he were fortunate, a train journey on the Grand Trunk Pacific Railway.

House calls were different in those days and, by their very nature, may have injected a certain tranquility into the hectic life of a frontier family doctor. In spring and summer a call from someone on the road to Fort St James, perhaps five or 10 miles away, would necessitate a two-hour drive. In the early evening he could be seen making his way in his buggy, medical bag back of the seat, reins in one hand, and a buggy whip in the other. While his team carried him along, Dr Stone could take in the beauty that lay about him. The soft hum of the insects, the evening song of robins and meadow larks, the strident calls of the crow all warned him to stay away from nests built into the trees along the narrow wagon road. All about nature burst forth. Flowers abounded along either side of the trail: wild roses, Indian paintbrush, daisies, fragrant clover, and wild columbine. Betimes the horse broke wind and acrid equine fumes mixed with the perfumes of the flowers.

When Dr Stone arrived at a log home and made his entrance to the welcome of people who were well known to him, his very presence seemed to effect a kind of cure. Most of the illnesses that he saw were of the common variety that any family doctor would see, but certainly there were more serious illnesses as well. Among other things, he treated diphtheria, scarlet fever, tonsillitis, gastrointestinal upsets, typhoid fever, respiratory problems associated with bronchitis and pneumonia, appendicitis, kidney stones, abscesses, and fractures and dislocations. These were either handled in the home or the patient was brought back to Vanderhoof. Many operations were performed under kitchen-table circumstances.

As has been mentioned, in the early days there were practically no useful medicines. Ether and chloroform were reasonably good anesthetics, although somewhat dangerous by modern standards. Morphine was available and was effective for pain (it remains one of our best medications to this day). Digitalis was available for heart failure, and a variety of medications were used for urinary tract infections.

Venereal disease was also a problem, and arsenic was used to treat syphilis. This was the main ingredient in Salvarsan (also called 606—The Magic Bullet). It was not very efficacious for the eradication of syphilis and left radio-opaque deposits in the patients' butts— deposits that would still be visible fifty years later. A mixture of potassium citrate was not very effective medicine for gonorrhea, and I note that among Dr Stone's instruments was a urethral dilator for correcting the narrowing of strictures, a condition that often occurs after a bout of gonorrhea (also known as glanders, clap, or old Joe).

Dr Stone was active in establishing an immunization program in schools, and, indeed, a diphtheria vaccine was available at that time, as were tetanus and smallpox vaccinations. The latter was particularly important, since in 1862 and 1892 there had been severe, decimating smallpox epidemics in the Vanderhoof area. On Dr Stone's arrival in Vanderhoof he established the first drugstore in partnership with Mr Graham Knight. This was later sold to the pharmacist Mr Mitchell.

In addition to treating medical conditions, Dr Stone had a busy surgical practice. Many of his operations were conducted under the most primitive conditions. The instruments he used included scalpels, hemostats (for clamping off blood vessels), dissecting scissors, small retractors, and puncturing instruments such as trochars and syringes. For difficult maternity cases obstetric forceps were available, and for orthopaedic operations pins, mallets, and bone saws were used.

A nurse, or sometimes a helper, gave open-drop ether for anaesthetic. A testimony to Dr Stone's good judgement and skill is the fact that his patients had few complications after surgery and that it was an extremely rare occasion when he actually lost a patient.

Practising in a small frontier village has many rewards, all of which stem from the trust and appreciation of one's patients. Anyone who was seriously stricken or who had loved ones dying remembered Dr Stone's kindly, caring manner. One case that weighed particularly on him was that of a friend, Jim Campbell, who died from tuberculosis. There was simply no effective medication for this disease at that time.

Patients who were seriously ill caused Dr Stone terrible stress and worry. And there were no consultants to call in to help him carry the burden. Many nights he could be seen walking the floors, his movements visible against the backdrop of the gaslight or coal-oil lamps. At these times his daughter told me that he would snap his fingers repetitively to relieve as much tension as possible. Other times a bowl of corn flakes and milk seemed to fortify him for the stresses of late-night crises. Ross Stone, in addition to his busy general practice, was also the doctor for the railway, for public health, and for the schools. For a number of years he was also Vanderhoof's coroner.

One event in which Dr Stone was involved had international ramifications and was probably the result of feelings that dated back to the Austro-Hungarian Empire. At any rate, this event occurred following the First World War. Two Europeans met an Austrian

Dr Ross Stone and his three little "Pebbles" 1922.
Courtesy of Marg Calvert.

immigrant who had holdings north of Vanderhoof around Trembleur
Lake. The three journeyed from Vanderhoof up into the wilds, and
the two recent immigrants never returned. This was in the fall of
the year, and, when their absence was eventually noticed, the
Austrian settler could give no satisfactory explanation as to their
whereabouts. Dr Stone, as coroner, and two policemen travelled the
60 miles north to Trembleur Lake and eventually found two graves.
The decapitated bodies of the European visitors were unearthed,
and it was apparent that they had been murdered. The limbs of their
bodies had been removed to enable them to be fit into two small
graves. Dr Stone performed autopsies under the most rudimentary
conditions, determined that the two men had been murdered, and
established the cause of death. The Austrian settler was brought to
justice and hanged. Dr Stone's daughter, Margaret Calvert, relates
that the overalls that he had worn during the autopsies were hung
in the back shed over the winter and that Mrs Stone was most upset
about this. The family avoided that area of their home for months.

And what of Dr Stone? Where did he derive the spiritual and
emotional resources to cope with the tremendous stresses that were
laid upon him? He was a descendent of United Empire Loyalists.
Approximately 200 years before his birth his family had immigrated
first to the eastern United States and then, following the American
Revolution, to Ontario, and finally to Cartwright, Manitoba (a small

village in the Portage La Prairie area), where he was born. His father, Levi Webster Stone, had brought his mother, Marianne, to a Manitoba farm from Ontario. When Ross was a child his family made its way west, first to Tacoma, Washington, and then to Vancouver, British Columbia. In Vancouver young Ross helped maintain the family and earned his own spending money by delivering papers. A number of energetic lads of his age were in the same business and went on to fame and fortune—one of them being Cyclone Taylor, the famous hockey player and wealthy entrepreneur.

Ross went to Vancouver College, graduated with honours, and then went on to McGill University, where he excelled and, upon graduating, received the gold medal in obstetrics. During summer breaks from university Ross Stone worked in the survey crews in the Prince Rupert area as well as on the Grand Trunk Pacific Railway, which was being extended eastwards from the Coast. After graduation he interned in Montreal and in Vancouver General Hospital. He then harkened to an adventurous spirit and made his way north to the Hazelton area, were he worked with Dr Horace Wrinch for 16 months. He was in town to assist with the medical problems resulting from the big Hazelton bank robbery and shootout mentioned in Chapter 5.

The last spike was driven for the Grand Trunk Pacific Railway just east of Fort Fraser in April 1914, and Dr Stone moved his practice to Endako. Then, sensing more opportunity in a developing community called Vanderhoof, he moved his practice there to better serve Fort St James to the north, Stoney Plains to the south, and the settlements back and forth along the railways.

In 1916 he returned to Montreal and married Susan MacDonald, his sweetheart from university days. Like his father before him, he brought his new bride to a far frontier. It meant a community of scattered log houses, dusty roads in the summer, icy roads in the winter, and muddy roads the rest of the time. It also meant a log house without a sewer connection, outhouses, no hot and cold running water, no washing machines, and the bearing and raising children far from extended family support. Perhaps the wives were the real pioneers, the doctors at least being privy to many "manly" comforts in this rural setting.

At any rate, both Ross and Susan had the courage to go into an isolated community far from sophisticated resources, either medical or social. Susan stood by her husband in times of extreme worry and stress, and she served the community by advising and teaching mothers as well as by being a public health nurse.

Dr Stone did not to have a son to follow in his footsteps, but his three daughters maintained his standing and reputation. He was heard to say that his wife was not going to fill a house with daughters in an attempt to have a son. The eldest, Margaret, was a registered nurse and served overseas with the Canadian forces, arriving home in 1946. Shortly after this Dr Stone died from renal disease compounded by heart complications.

Dr Stone's greatest memorial is found in the hearts and minds of the people in the area that he served. Perhaps one of the memorials dearest to him was the modern hospital established in Vanderhoof. He describes the day of its opening as the happiest day of his life. In addition, the Dr Ross Stone Memorial Scholarship was established at the University of Victoria. Ross Stone brought honour to himself, to his family, and to the whole medical profession.

University of Victoria
Victoria, British Columbia

The President's Regional Entrance Scholarship

The University of Victoria offers annually four entrance scholarships within each college region in British Columbia to students with high academic standing and broad interests. These are called the President's Regional Entrance Scholarships. In order to increase the identification of each scholarship with a particular college region and to honor a person of regional historical significance, the scholarships are named after men and women who contributed to the advancement and development of the region and its people and who were highly respected members of their community. The name of Dr. Ross Stone was one of those selected to represent the College of New Caledonia Region.

CHAPTER 15

Susan Viola Stone:
From Montreal To Vanderhoof

Susan Viola Stone, c.1918.
Courtesy of Margaret Calvert.

Mount Royal in the centre of Montreal, Quebec, is a far cry from the flat, prairie-like terrain of Vanderhoof. In 1916 this was accepted cheerfully by Susan Stone when she accompanied her frontier doctor husband from Montreal to Vanderhoof. They were never to go together to Montreal again.

Susan was the third child of Maggie and John Macdonald of Leguere, Quebec. Their rural farm home was large and comfortable, and on their property was a church and store. Tragedy struck when Susan was 10, and her father died after a short illness. The family then moved from the farm to Montreal. After finishing high school, both Susan and her brother Dal went to McGill University, where Susan received her BA in education and her brother studied medicine.

It was at McGill that a young westerner, Ross Stone, initially came to her attention through his friendship with her brother. After graduating from McGill in 1912, Susan taught school in Montreal for three years. During that time Ross Stone began practising medicine—first in Hazelton, then in Endako, and finally in Vanderhoof.

Susan's daughter, Margaret Stone, says that Susan and Ross were married on April 25, 1916, in Valleyfield, Quebec. After the usual wedding glitches, including the failure of the flowers to arrive, the happy couple set off to Niagara Falls and then went straight on to Vanderhoof. For years they said that they were still on their honeymoon.

They were met at the Grand Trunk Pacific Railway station by an old friend, Sam Cocker, and his horse and buggy. The horse, named Gertie, sat down in a large puddle on the way to the newlyweds' first house (she was known to have some unusual characteristics). There is no record that Susan was unduly shocked by the mud and dust of Vanderhoof. Young love truly does make up for a lot of problems with one's surroundings, such as deep mud in the spring, dusty roads in the summer and fall, and 40-degree-below-zero weather in the winter. Not to mention the clouds of mosquitoes in the summer, along with no-see-ums, deer flies, horseflies, and bugs of all sorts. Fortunately, the mosquitoes did not carry malaria, and the bugs were only a minor nuisance.

Prior to his marriage, Ross and his brother Cliff had added three rooms onto the original log cabin, which resided on 40 acres along the Nechako River. Initially, there was outdoor plumbing only, and washing was done by hand. Water came from a handpump in the kitchen. This rather primitive facility did not affect the young couple's enjoyment of life one bit. Life was a lot of fun, with young people around for picnics, dances, and even a buggy trip 40 miles north to Fort St James. Relatives visited, and there were many social occasions involving dances, dinners, and card-playing evenings.

Susan did not become involved in medical practice to a large extent, primarily because a year later baby girls started arriving: Margaret in June 1917, Helen in July 1918, and Molly in August 1919. Susan said that she thought she would have a baby girl every 13 months for the rest of her life. However Ross, as mentioned in Chapter 14, said that they weren't going to fill the house with girls just to get a boy, so that was the family—three little girls, whom people delighted in referring to as Dr Stone's three little pebbles (a joke that the "pebbles" did not think was tremendously funny).

Having babies in Vanderhoof was not the most fulfilling experience for a young wife from Montreal, separated from members of her extended family. The first baby was born some 200 miles to the west in Hazelton, which had the nearest hospital (and, by modern standards, it was a poor facility for the birth of first babies). Helen, the second baby, was also born in Hazelton, while Molly was born only 60 miles from home in a Prince George hospital.

While Susan Stone did not participate in the practice of medicine, as did other wives, she was a tower of strength at home, providing support and a happy married life for Dr Stone. Her life revolved around her home and Dr Stone's work and needs. Her husband came first, but her children were immediately behind. And they accepted this cheerfully. Margaret remembers her mother getting up when Dr Stone was called in the middle of the night. She put hot coals from the kitchen fire in a foot warmer so that his feet might be kept warm in the horse-drawn cutter.

Life in Vanderhoof progressed happily. A young Native girl, Victorine Sam, was hired to help in the home. Modern conveniences were acquired, and Susan Stone was active in the Ladies' Aid (a church-affiliated group), the Red Cross, the school board, and, around 1927, a women's hockey team.

In 1920 the family acquired its first radio. There were shows such as *Amos 'n' Andy*, *The Little Red School House*, *Fibber Magee and Molly*—all of which were popular for many years. Susan enjoyed dancing, and the couple went to most of the local dances. The last dance they danced together was to the tune of "Alice's Blue Gown." This was in December 1945 at the big welcome-home dance for soldiers returning from the Second World War.

After the war, 30 years of married life were to end with the untimely passing of Dr Stone. Susan spent her years in Vancouver, Salmon Arm, and, again, in Vanderhoof, giving love and support to her three daughters and to her grandchildren. This was, in some respects, a lonely time for her, but she endured with fortitude and courage. A copy of a letter sent to her in 1954 gives evidence of her continuing concern for the people of the Vanderhoof area. A Mrs Hilda Bergstrom wrote to thank Susan for her help in compiling records so that a birth certificate could be issued: "I have no way of expressing my thanks in full, but I hope you will accept my most grateful thanks for all you have done for me."

Susan Stone left many happy memories to her community and family. Quebec gave us a worthy pioneer, wife, mother, and community advocate.

CHAPTER 16

Dr Carl Ewert of Prince George

Dr Carl Ewert: Founder of modern
medicine in Prince George.

Truly God moves in mysterious ways, and this was particularly so
with regard to certain Winnipeg parents. It was their devotion to
their God and their attention to the schooling of their children that
brought an outstanding doctor to Prince George—Dr Carl Ewert. In
1890 the Mennonite School system in Winnipeg was in an uproar
over the introduction of certain practices that it felt to be threatening.
One was the use of English as the language of instruction; others
were recommendations for government funding of Mennonite schools
and the introduction of certain science courses. The Old Colony and
Bergthal Mennonites were very upset by this; the more liberal Kleine
Gemeinde less so.

The only solution was to bring in an outsider from Kansas, the Reverend Heinrich Ewert. He was a Mennonite and a respected teacher, pastor, and diplomat who was known and acceptable to the Winnipeg Brethren but neutral regarding the furore over the school system. He was particularly favoured because of his kinship with the beloved missionary to China, Elizabeth Goerz. The decision to bring Ewart to Winnipeg was to have far-reaching consequences, for it brought a wealth of talent to Canada. Among members of the Ewert family was the child who later became Dr Carl Ewert—the man who was to lay the foundation for modern medicine in Fort George and Prince George.

Carl Ewert was born in Halsted, Kansas, on August 10, 1886, the second oldest of five children born to Reverend and Mrs H. Henrich Ewert. In 1891 the family moved to the Winnipeg area, where Carl's father was the principal of the Mennonite Normal School at Gretna and the promoter and inspector of the Mennonite schools in his district.

All five siblings took up professions. Carl's older brother Paul went into medicine and practised for many years in Golden, BC. Bill went through dental school and practised in both Manitoba and British Columbia. Alfred was a Rhodes Scholar who stayed in Oxford, England, as a Professor of Romance Languages. The youngest in the family was Elma, who, besides studying to be a concert pianist, was a registered nurse.

Carl received a bachelor of science degree from the University of Manitoba and was the silver medalist in his graduating class. Following this, he studied medicine at McGill, earning his MD in 1910. As well as having an excellent scholastic record, he was active in athletics and was a member of the McGill hockey team. On November 10, 1911, Carl registered with the College of Physicians and Surgeons of British Columbia.

"Doc," as he was affectionately called, practised for a short period of time in Nanaimo. Eventually he travelled over the Royal Engineers' Cariboo Road as far as Soda Creek and then took the old *BX* paddle wheeler up the Fraser River to central Fort George. He arrived there on June 2, 1913. He is reported to have climbed the long flight of stairs leading from the river to the top of the cliff, to have looked at all the flags and bunting that had been hung in the little town to honour the birthday of King George V, and to have said: "How did they know I would be here today?"

Shortly after his arrival, he became associated with Drs Swenerton and McSorley. Their practice covered a large and isolated area, and

Prince George, BC, c.1920.
Courtesy of Shirley Ennest.

travelling to visit their patients was not always easy. If there was a road, travel would be by a horse and buggy hired from Billy Corbet's livery stable in Fort George. At other times, they would take the railroad speeder and stay with a patient until his or her crisis was over (usually two or three days).

In 1915, Dr Ewert moved his practice one mile from Fort George to nearby Prince George, where he worked and was active in community affairs for many years. His office was on Third Avenue, near George Street, on the second floor of what was then the old Assman Block. Carl was primarily interested in practising obstetrics, medicine, and anaesthesia, and he frequently gave anaesthetic for Dr E.J. Lyon, a surgeon who arrived in Prince George in 1918. When required, Dr Ewert also practised veterinary medicine and frequently immunized dogs to protect them from distemper.

Mrs Isabel Ford of Prince George recalls the time in 1916 when her father had rheumatic fever. Dr Ewert visited him nine times and gave him several injections. This was prior to the completion of the Cameron Street Bridge. As Mrs Ford's father and family lived on the North Nechako, directly across from the end of George Street, Dr Ewert had to use a rowboat to cross the river. The rower was none other than he himself. Mrs Ford's father was bedridden from August 13 to October 3. On July 9, 1918, Dr Ewert delivered Margaret, Mrs Ford's sister. Sadly, she died of pneumonia on September 21, 1918, in the great flu epidemic.

J.R. Van Somer (Jimmy), an old-timer from Prince George and Fort Ware, recalls having Dr Ewert as a physician and credits him with saving his life. Many years ago, Jimmy was hauling coal in the Hudson's Hope area, when he became very ill. He had a fever, cough, chest pain, and was coughing up blood. He spent a week in a Fort St John hotel and found his room very cold. He then stayed with friends at Link Creek, near Hudson's Hope, for a further week. He was beginning to feel better, so he returned home to Prince George. However, there he felt on the verge of collapse, and an old friend and former employer, Richard Corless Jr, insisted he go to hospital.

Dr Ewert saw him at the hospital and diagnosed pleurisy with fluid on the left lung. Jimmy was taken into a surgical room where he noted a big tray of surgical instruments. Dr Ewert advised him that these instruments were required for the surgical procedure to be performed on his chest. A surgical prep was carried out, and he was then given half a shot of brandy by the matron, Dorothy Saunders. Dr Ewert, all the while whistling calmly through his teeth (whenever he made house calls, his imminent arrival could be predicted upon hearing this trademark whistling), inserted a long needle into Jimmy's left chest. Apparently the procedure was quite painful, but a large amount of fluid was removed and the patient, much improved, left the hospital four days later. Jimmy remembered Dr Ewert as a cheerful, caring, and always available doctor.

In 1918, when the flu epidemic hit, Dr Ewert and Dr Lyon were the only doctors in Prince George. The city hospital could not accommodate all the ill people, so the schools and the old Princess Theatre were taken over and used to house very sick patients. Only on November 18, 1918, when the number of flu cases had declined, were the schools re-opened. Dr Ewert vaccinated many of the children in the Central Fort George area and Mud River schools. He told friends that his best nurse was a Miss Harvey (a former Klondike gold rush gal and a great friend of Isabel Ford's mother), who had no nurses' training.

Romance came into Carl Ewert's life when, in 1923, he married Natannis Reid. She made a marvellous wife and mother. They had two children: Katherine, now living in Federal Way, Washington, and Robert, now living in Prince George.

The doctor practised through the Depression when, in spite of there being much unemployment and people having little or no money, various illnesses and emergencies continued to occur. Even though people did not have money, their illnesses were always treated. Indeed, many of Dr Ewert's works proved to be errands of mercy and labours of love rather than works of monetary profit. Payment of fees was frequently made in the form of firewood, and the Ewert's backyard was literally filled with beautiful birchwood. Another favourite method of payment was the delivery of live chickens—never cleaned or plucked, always live. To accommodate the live fowl, a makeshift chicken coop was built in the backyard. Potatoes,

Dr Carl Ewert, Referee with a cowbell.
"Five minutes for roughing."
Courtesy of FFGRM.

vegetables, and many other commodities were also delivered to the Ewerts' door.

Dr Ewert was Medical Health Officer for the Prince George and District School Board, and, once or twice a year, he visited all the schools in the district, performing physical examinations on the pupils. According to Elizabeth Sinclair, then a 10-year-old pupil, now a retired senior citizen, she refused to remove her blouse. "I wasn't going to let him look at my little buttons." This modesty seems now to have been lost

Dr Ewert was a member of the Board of Directors of the Health League of Canada and was district representative for the Central Interior of British Columbia. His fraternal affiliations were with the Masonic Lodge, the Elks, and the Rotary Club of Prince George. He had the distinction of being installed as Exalted Ruler of the local Elks Club in January 1933. During October 1942 the Rotary Club of Prince George was formed, and Dr Carl Ewert was elected as its first president. Always a staunch Liberal, he was a strong supporter of the Honourable Harry G. Perry, a former Minister of Education and Speaker of the Legislature.

Dr Ewert was a keen sportsman and enjoyed fishing, small game hunting, and athletics. He was an avid golfer and was named "Premier Golfer of the Cariboo" during Labour Day weekend, 1934. The tournament was held in Prince George, and his prize was the Rod MacKenzie Cup. He played at the Prince George golf course, which is now Fort George Park. The course had no greens as we know them. Actually, they were sand greens, and, after completing a hole, the sand had to be raked over in preparation for the golfers that followed. He was a regular curler at the two-sheet curling club at the foot of Connaught Hill. He excelled as a hockey player and, later, as an official referee in the Cariboo Hockey League.

In those days hockey was played in an open-air rink located near the centre of town. The rink was owned by the city and managed by a well-known gentleman named Harry Thacker. With the large snowfalls that sometimes occurred before a practice or a game, the ice had to be cleared by scraper and shovel. On occasion, when Carl was refereeing a game, the weather would be so cold that his whistle would freeze up. Undaunted, he would use a cowbell to call penalties. He was known for having two signs—two fingers and five fingers—meaning two minutes for tripping and five minutes for fighting, respectively.

He was also a doctor for the local hockey team. One day, one of the players came to him, as he was concerned about having contracted a "social disease." He told Dr Ewert that he may or may not have VD, he wasn't sure. Dr Ewert examined him and then said, "I'll put your mind at rest, Bill, you've got it alright."

Dr and Mrs Ewert were very active in the social life of the community and always went to the fore in any event that had to do with the improvement of people's lives. Dr Ewert maintained a busy practice in Prince George until 1946, at which time he retired due to failing health. His practice was taken over by Dr L.T. Maxwell.

Prior to leaving Prince George, several testimonial dinners were given in honour of Dr and Mrs Ewert. In July 1946 Dr Ewert was guest of honour at a dinner sponsored by the Prince George Hockey Club. He was recognized as a player, referee, club official, and fan during his long association with hockey in Prince George. Many old-timers—such as Harry Thacker, Ivor Guest, Walter Flynn, and Claude Foot—attended the dinner. Many of those in attendance expressed their regret at Carl's impending departure from the community.

Dr Ewert was given credit for spearheading the construction of the new covered rink, which was located on the present site of the Simon Fraser Hotel. On behalf of the club, players, and fans, Dr Ewert was presented with a Parker 5 fountain pen. And in July 1946 Dr Ewert was recognized by the Prince George and District Liberals for his 20 years of service as president of the association. As a thank you, Mr H.G. Perry presented Carl with a gold watch.

During August 1946, more honours were bestowed on Dr and Mrs Ewert by the Rotary and Elks Clubs. Mr Harold Assman, President of the Rotary Club, wished its charter president and his wife good health, happiness, and bon voyage. Mr H.G. Perry, a charter member of the BPO Elks Lodge No. 122, bestowed on Dr Ewert the title of "Good Citizen." He also presented Carl with a gold lodge pin and Natannis with a white handbag.

Dr Robert Ewert, Carl's son, is a fellowship surgeon who returned to care for the people of Prince George, where he is now retired. The old family residence at the corner of Seventh Avenue and Vancouver Street is now the location of the famous Rosel's Restaurant.

Carl and Natannis retired to Burquitlam, where they purchased a two-acre plot. This gave Carl a chance to relax and once again tend to his beloved vegetable garden. He passed away in 1954 and was sadly missed by his family and wide circle of friends. A great man, he left his mark on Prince George as both a doctor and a community leader.

The Ewert house at 7th and Vancouver in Prince George
is now a popular restaurant.

CHAPTER 17

Giscome and Prince George:
Dr Edwin James Lyon

Dr. Edwin Lyon, c.1948.
From original print, Prince George Regional Hospital.

One of the most competent and colourful medical personalities in the Prince George area was, without a doubt, Dr Edwin "Flying Eddie" James Lyon. The gruff exterior of this big man concealed a nature that was compassionate, gentle, and humourous. And he was one of the great surgeons in British Columbia.

Dr Lyon was born in 1880 and was educated in a Guelph public school. He attended the University of Toronto, from which he graduated in 1905 with a medical degree. He continued his studies in London, England, where he did two years of postgraduate work in a London hospital followed by two years at the general hospital in Birmingham. While in England he became a Member of the Royal

College of Surgeons and a Licentiate of the Royal College of Physicians.

Prior to coming to north-central BC he had established a busy practice in Winnipeg. On November 5, 1917, he was registered by the College of Physicians and Surgeons of British Columbia and came north to Giscome, where he was employed by the Frost Lumber Company. Near the end of 1918 he set up practice in Prince George. At that time the only other physician in the community was Dr Carl Ewert. These two doctors practised here for many years before being joined by a third physician—Dr Harold Trefry.

Dr Lyon was a trained surgeon, probably a born surgeon. He was fast, decisive, and possessed impeccable clinical judgement. His medical career spanned the days from no antibiotics or blood transfusions to the present. He was competent in a number of fields of surgery that are now separated into subspecialties. Dr Lyon performed surgery in what would now be classed as general surgery, urology, gynaecology, obstetrics, orthopaedics, and neuro-surgery. Dr Leonard Maxwell, a current fellowship surgeon, learned much from Dr Lyon and credited him with being a surgeon second to none—past or present.

Dr Lyon, or Eddie, as he was affectionately called, held many positions of note during his years in Prince George. Some of these were as follows: (1) Representative of the Department of Pensions and National Health; (2) Physician to the Prince George Indian Band; (3) Civil Aviation Physician; (4) Prison Physician; (5) President of the local branch of the Canadian Medical Association (his executive consisted of the well-known medical pioneers of the area—Dr Gerald Rumsey Baker of Quesnel was vice-president, Dr Carl Ewert was secretary/treasurer, and Drs Steele and Trefry of Prince George were directors); (6) Vice-President of the BC Medical Association; (7) Director of the Medical Services Association of BC; (8) Certificant of the Royal College of Surgeons of Canada, February 1947, (this became one of his most prized possessions): (9) Honorary member of the Surgical Society of BC: and (10) President of the College of Physicians and Surgeons of BC.

Dr Lyon was forthright and sincere, and he had a large practice and many friends. He was widely respected and known for his social work. He always participated enthusiastically in any community endeavour. There are many anecdotes concerning his years of practice. In her letter of tribute, the late Gladys Boehler expressed the opinion of his many patients:

When I was twelve years old I was on the CNR train returning from Edmonton with my family, and while at Jasper station fainted. When I woke up I was in a berth packed with ice and on the way to Prince George. At the time there was no doctor in Jasper, so by some means of communication, instructions were given regarding the ice-packing. The porter took charge, even my mother had a back seat. On arrival in Prince George I remember a very loud voice asking: Where is she?" The porter answering, "Here, here," and the berth curtains flew open and here into focus came Dr Lyon, and he looked like a giant to me. He whipped the covers off, rolled me in a blanket, picked me up and carried me out to his car, put me in the back seat, and it seemed, we flew to the hospital. When we arrived I was in his arms again, and he was packing me up the front steps, all the while roaring orders all the way into the hospital and operating room.

The last thing that I remember was the smell of ether. I had suffered a ruptured appendix. He pulled me through, and I'm sure that the strength of his voice reassuring me after the operation had a lot to do with it. He actually told me over and over, "Hang on there, Baby, hang on, Baby!" I can still hear it to this day. After I went home he came regularly to the house to remove and replace packing. While he was attending me he would whistle, "Claire de la Lune." This song was forever to remind me of him, plus the smell of ether.

Thus began a long patient-doctor relationship between a child and a physician who always had time to talk and listen. She recounts a further episode that gives an indication of this doctor's grasp of human nature as well as of the subtleties of nature's role in our defence against diseases. She was invited to the Lyons' home for tea, and when she arrived she found Dr Lyon, his dog, and one small boy sitting on the kitchen floor. The three of them were sharing cookies. The doctor would take a bite, then the dog would take a bite, then the boy would take a bite. Dr Lyon looked up and said, "I'm immunizing this boy. His mother has kept him so damn sterile, he picks up everything that comes along." This little act was carried out until everyone had had enough cookies. I was told to be sure and let my kids play in the dirt and not to worry if they ate mud pies.

Nothing went by in Prince George without Dr Lyon being aware of it. He knew everyone in town and always had time for a chat. According to Gladys Boehler: "One day when I was 17 I had dressed up in a suit and hat and gloves to go to a tea. While walking down George Street, thinking I looked just super, Dr Lyon drove by, stuck his head out of the car, and yelled: 'Gladys, you look great, but your blouse ties are hanging below your suit coat.' I was sure everyone on the street heard him, and I walked on with a very red face."

Catherine Cadden, born January 6, 1905, spoke very highly of Dr Lyon. Now a 91-year-old woman, she describes him as a good and humane doctor who looked after her family wonderfully well and saw her through a her first home delivery and the hospital deliveries of her other children, including a set of twins. Mrs Cadden remembers him suturing up a severe thigh laceration (incurred by her daughter Jean in a playing accident) as well as his expertise in pulling teeth.

Mrs Isabel Ford, a pioneer of Prince George, remembers him attending her sister Margaret Tyner, who had pneumonia. He also operated on her mother in November 1918 for what appeared to be a tumour of the womb. While the mother was convalescing she noticed Dr Lyon pacing the halls and whistling "Rescue the Perishing." Apparently he was preparing to do surgery on a patient with a brain tumour. He carried out the surgery and the patient made a good recovery. Further to this, on August 30, 1920, the first Caesarean section in Prince George was performed by Dr Lyon, as he was the only physician in the city. A baby girl, Peggy Traquair, was delivered and all went well. In 1930 Dr Lyon married Nancy Barbara Allyn, a former matron of the Prince George Hospital. Miss Allyn was his second wife, his first marriage having foundered. There were two children from his first marriage, however: James and Patricia.

His nickname, "Flying Eddie," was a result of his passion for driving large, fast cars at top speed. These cars suffered occasional collisions with a "silent policeman," a traffic signal at the corner of Third and George Streets, consisting of a concrete base with vertical pillar. His driving peculiarities came in handy one day in a bizarre shooting incident, which occurred right outside his clinic door on George Street. A young Native named Jimmy was out to get Max, a taxi driver, who apparently had formed an attachment to Jimmy's wife. One day Jimmy, armed with a rifle, spotted his rival on George

Dr Edwin Lyon (centre) with famous motor car.
Courtesy of FFGRM.

Street, took aim, and fired one accurate shot. Max was hit in the left shoulder, knocked over, and lay bleeding profusely on the ground. Jimmy then turned the gun on himself and fired his second shot. Dr Eddie Lyon, having heard the shots, opened his office door and spotted the two casualties lying in the street. He grabbed a handful of haemostats, rushed out the door, and attended to both men, stopping Max's haemorrhage and probably saving his life. He then loaded both of them into the back seat of his touring sedan and raced to the hospital. Both men survived, but Max wound up with a paralysed left arm and Jimmy had to have his left arm amputated.

When Jimmy wakened from the anaesthetic he was most upset that he was still alive. Then he noticed his arm was missing, which was also upsetting. However, his main concern was his diamond ring. He exclaimed, "My diamond ring, where is it? It was on my finger!" A nurse was dispatched to the incinerator to search for the ring. The amputated limb was lying in the incinerator, which, fortunately, had not been fired up. The nurse recovered the arm, removed the bandages, and, lo and behold, on one of the fingers was a ring containing the largest diamond she had ever seen. The ring was given back to Jimmy, who was most thankful for its return. Jimmy survived for only two months after this shooting episode, but the durable Max recovered and continued to live in Prince George for many years.

Dr Lyon was known as an outdoorsman, and many of his most pleasant vacations were spent camped by one of the area's large lakes. He had a great love of nature and an interest in and knowledge of the wild flowers of the area. Mrs Gladys Boehler mentions that during the summer there was always a bouquet of wild flowers gracing the dining table in his tent or home: "I often wondered about this big, gruff man and his love for something as tiny and dainty as a lady's slipper." She remembers that every spring it was a ritual with him to race down the Hart Highway in his touring car to gather a bunch of wild lupine.

Dr Lyon loved to cook, and he loved his meat rare and rather high. Jimmy Friend gave him four grouse one weekend after a hunt. A week later he saw the doctor and asked him if the grouse had been enjoyed. "Not yet," replied Dr Lyon. "They are still buried, but will be ready in two days." He dug them up right before eating them. He was known to have meat kept hanging at the butcher's for days before cooking it.

One adventure nearly finished the famous doctor. In August of 1944 he and Mrs Lyon, together with a niece from Edmonton and another couple, narrowly escaped drowning. They were caught in the worst storm to sweep Stuart Lake in years. Seeking sanctuary from the torment of the mounting waves that pounded their cabin cruiser, they found a small bay opposite Battleship Island, about two miles north of Fort St James. The boat was swept onto the beach by giant waves that proceeded to pounded it to pieces. The party, while possessing ample provisions, was without blankets and huddled together in a tiny tent throughout a stormy night. They were eventually sighted by a Native, who took the doctor to Fort St. James in his small boat then returned and rescued the women and children. On his return to Prince George, Dr Lyon commented, "I've been through many experiences, but this is the first time I've ever been shipwrecked."

In 1949 the *Prince George Citizen* commented on Dr Lyon's role as the local jail doctor. The jail was in the basement of the government building downtown on the corner of Brunswick Street and Third Avenue. When Dr Lyon had finished examining the inmates, he attempted to leave but found himself locked in the cell with them. The attendants had retired upstairs for coffee. After close to half an hour of fuming and pacing up and down in a locked cell, Dr Lyon thrust his arms through the bars of the door and smashed the fire alarm to draw attention to his plight. Almost immediately the government official, fire chief, and firemen arrived in a panic, looking for smoke and fire. Dr Lyon, in considerable temper, pointed out the shortcomings of their attendants and, on his release, received profuse apologies from all.

Eddie was well known as an organist, and his music was a regular feature of a local radio station. He was always in demand and knew by heart the old songs that people in the district appreciated so much. One of the most memorable and anticipated events during the Christmas season involved listening to Dr Lyon playing Christmas carols on his organ, with his windows wide open so that the whole neighbourhood could enjoy this musical treat. As Prince George had at that time a population of between 1,500 and 2,000, almost everyone in the city could listen.

A piano was kept in the hospital, and on many occasions Dr Lyon pressed it into use in order to present a musical interlude to the staff and the patients. He claimed that playing the piano kept his fingers nimble for his surgical operations.

For 31 years Dr Lyon served his city, but in 1949 an abdominal condition, probably diverticulitis, gave him increasingly severe symptoms. He was moved to Vancouver where he was under the care of Dr Roy Huggard, and he underwent surgery on March 14. He appeared to be making a normal recovery but suffered a relapse and died within a few days. The likely cause of his death was a perforation of the bowel, which brought with it acute complications from peritonitis and shock.

The funeral took place in Vancouver, with the clergy of St James officiating and with many Prince George residents in attendance to help bear the burden of sadness and grief experienced by his wife and family. Among the many tributes to Dr Lyon was a letter from Dr Roy Huggard that was published in the *Prince George Citizen* (7 April, 1949, 3) Dr Huggard eulogizes his friend and colleague as follows:

> *The late Dr E.J. Lyon held a singular position in his profession in this province. It may be truly said that he was a pioneer in the great northern hinterland in providing the advances of modern surgery as we consider them to the isolated areas during the early days. He was characterized by inflexible honesty and had acquired a large advanced training during his 4 years abroad as a young man. Had he chosen to*

remain in one of the large centers of Canada, he would have achieved a distinction and fame of national character. His life, however, was for the community in which he lived the greater half of it. No man had a higher reputation within the confines of his own calling, not only as a man but as one gifted with a greater degree of skill than the average. Above all he possessed in adequate degree, that strange intangible quality that we frequently refer to as the "art of medicine." The healing profession in its fullest sense is truly a combination of science and art, in both he was richly endowed.

So passed from our midst a great man and a great doctor, loved and respected by the city that he had served so well. We shall not see his like again.

CHAPTER 18

Dr Arch Gray
and The Lake District Of Central BC

First Hospital, Lake District, Keefe farm.
Courtesy of Alice Keefe.

The lakes district of central BC may seem isolated, yet from 1910 onward it was the centre of thriving agricultural and logging operations, which were soon to be linked to market by rail and roads. In 1919 there was a hospital located in a converted log home on Keefe's farm, south of Burns Lake. A year later the hospital was moved a mile away to Prosser Point on the shore of Francois Lake. It was at this time that Dr Arch Gray arrived from Formosa, where he had been a medical missionary.

The members of the Presbyterian Women's Missionary Society, located in Eastern Canada, had noted that the area south of Burns Lake was completely isolated a good part of the year and, with their minds, hearts, and pocketbooks, supported sending medical and spiritual care to the people of this area. Realizing that a hospital already existed, they appointed Dr Gray as the medical

Miss Kennedy, matron of First Hospital, Lake District.
Courtesy of Alice Keefe.

superintendent and Miss Mary Kennedy as the very proper matron
of the hospital.

Dr Gray could not have chosen a more unlikely spot to begin his
practice. His office was established in a log dwelling belonging to
John Keefe, he was 500 miles away from the nearest referral hospital,
and 15 miles from a rail link to the outside. Seven months of the
year a Francois Lake ferry connected the farming community of
South Bank to the north shore and Burns Lake; five months of the
year Francois Lake was covered in ice, which, depending on weather
conditions, may or may not have been crossable.

It was at Prosser Point that the first White child, Marian Keefe,
was born, and Dr Gray was in attendance, as was Miss Kennedy. A
second maternity case, a Mrs Newgard from Grassy Plains, was
monitored periodically in her tent on the perimeter of the hospital
grounds. It was while she was camped on the grounds of the hospital
that the latter was moved 15 miles to the north (see Chapter 10).

Dr Gray never refused to answer a call for medical assistance,
even if it might involve hours or sometimes days of arduous travel
by horse and buggy. This contrasted with the settlers' experiences
with railway construction camp doctors, who were forbidden to care
for patients not belonging to railway crews. Local people remembered

this with bitterness, and medical doctors like Arch Gray held a special place in their hearts.

The late Jean McKenna, born in 1913, remembered Dr Gray. Her brother Charles was born at the Prosser Point Hospital at Francois Lake, but when her sister Isabel was born the year before, her mother had to travel 130 miles to the hospital in Hazelton, as no local doctor was available. Mrs McKenna recounts that Dr Gray had a horse-drawn cutter, a small sleigh for winter travel, and a one-horse shay buggy for summer travel. Nothing was too much effort for him. On Wednesdays he drove his buggy into Burns Lake, some 15 miles away, to take calls and attend to medical needs. Burns Lake had neither resident doctor nor hospital.

Dr Gray was the only dentist in the area, and Mrs McKenna remembers that when he extracted a baby molar tooth she raised a terrible fuss and was ashamed of herself for the next 50 years. Dr Gray delivered a number of babies, set fractures, performed minor surgery, and generally attended to the medical needs of his people. Their spiritual needs were also his concern, and he led the Sunday service. Mrs McKenna remembers his sermons as well as his two children singing "Jesus Loves Me" in Chinese.

Life was hard and circumstances dealt harshly with Dr Gray. His wife died, leaving him with two small children. After moving to Vancouver he became an eye specialist and practised in the Dominion Bank Building. His son died as a young man, and his daughter developed a brain condition thought to be the aftermath of a viral infection contracted in the Far East. These pioneer missionary doctors and their families paid a great price, and honour is due them.

Jean McKenna related an incident involving her own health, and this gives one an indication of the fortitude of the frontier settlers:

> *I became very ill out across Francois Lake during spring break up. The doctor was unable to come until the ferry was able to run some days later. I had peritonitis in every organ but heart and lungs. He said he couldn't move me but put the bed at a slant with my head up. The next year I went the 160 miles to Prince George for an appendectomy by Dr Lyon. He found that my appendix had burst and had grown onto another loop of bowel. This is the way it was in the early days.*

For five years after Dr Gray left the Burns Lake area in 1924, it was intermittently served by locums. At times there was no doctor closer than Fort Fraser, which was 50 miles away. Mrs McKenna remembers that T.C. Holmes arrived in the late 1920s. He was a very competent surgeon and one of the last true pioneer doctors. During his many years of service at Burns Lake and the lake district he captured the affection and respect of the settlers. In time he attained the almost mystic stature of Dr Horace Wrinch of Hazelton and Dr Ross Stone of Vanderhoof.

CHAPTER 19

Medical Centre of The Cariboo

It is hard to imagine 150 Mile House as the medical centre of the Cariboo, yet during the years 1894 to 1918 it occupied just that position. The doctors were fully qualified and registered in BC. They all commanded respect and affection for their readiness to make house calls to the most isolated ranches—often one to two days travelling distance from 150 Mile House.

In 1900 there were no more than 300 inhabitants at 150 Mile, all scattered in homes along the Cariboo Wagon Road. A Russell fence on either side of the highway kept wandering cows and horses out of gardens and yards. Along the road came wagons, democrats, and saddle horses. Four-horse teams dragged dusty, heavy-laden dead X wagons over tortuous roads to Quesnel and Barkerville. From 150 Mile House a road went west to the Onward Ranch and then on to the Fraser River, the Chilcotin, and the Pacific Ocean 300 miles away.

Dr. R. T. Wilson Herald, Queens University, 1890. Front row, 3rd from right. Permission of Queens Archives.

To the east another road led to Beaver Valley, Horsefly, Likely, and Quesnelle Forks. From there a trail led over Yank Mountain to Barkerville.

Dr Hugh Watt, an 1880 graduate of the University of Toronto, served the 150 Mile House community on a locum basis starting in 1894. However Dr R.T. Wilson Herald was the first full-time medical practitioner in the area, and he arrived in the spring of 1896. His wife and sons, who were living in Ontario, did not accompany him.

Dr R.T. Wilson Herald, c. 1896.
Courtesy of John Roberts.

Dr Herald was a handsome, suave, 35-year-old Queen's University graduate. His Victorian-style full mustache set off handsome features, and he had a trim athletic build. An 1890 graduate from Queen's University, he was registered with the College of Physicians and Surgeons of British Columbia in 1891. He was an ear, nose, and throat specialist, first in Vancouver and then for a year in Ashcroft. When he stepped off the four-horse stagecoach in 150 Mile house after a three-day trip from Ashcroft, he was an experienced practitioner. Local people were seen either in his office or at their homes, while a rented team and buggy were used for distant house calls, which sometimes meant travelling up to 40 miles.

150 Mile House, c. 1870.
Courtesy of Williams Lake Museum.

Laura Moxan, an early Cariboo pioneer who is now gone, tells of an emergency appendectomy that Dr Herald performed on her father. Dr Herald was notified of John Moore's illness and travelled the 20 miles from 150 Mile House to Alkali Lake on a Howler (a two-wheel cart with ungreased wooden axels). On arrival, Dr Herald confirmed the diagnosis and used a table in the Moores' ranch home as an operating table. Following the operation the doctor remained with the family for several days, until John's recovery was assured. Laura mentions that all the Moore children were scared stiff.

Over the years of Dr Herald's residence at 150 Mile, babies were delivered, illnesses treated, and operations performed—most in the patients' own homes. One young miner was lost to pneumonia, and this led to the mining community having reduced confidence in Dr Herald. However, the nearest hospital was in Barkerville, and serious illnesses often led to fatal outcomes.

Dr Herald had access to morphine and opium; digitalis for heart failure; bromides as sleeping potions; and ether and chloroform as anaesthetics. Aspirin, a very useful drug, was known but not widely used. Most basic common surgical instruments were available, including pearl-handled scalpels, haemostats, retractors, bone saws, and improvised splints. Some practitioners had obstetrical forceps for difficult cases.

An amusing anecdote is attributed to Dr Herald. It seems that a Mrs Flett (a maid working for the Murphy family of nearby Deep Creek Ranch) was grossly overweight. Finally, after failing with diet and exercise, the doctor put her on the second floor of the store at

Original buildings, 150 Mile House, later destroyed by fire.
Courtesy of Williams Lake Museum.

150 Mile House and locked her in with a small portion of food—just enough to last her each day. Weeks went by without a pound of weight being lost. One evening the suspicious medical practitioner quietly walked around the building. He found his patient lustily hauling a pail of food from ground to second story by way of bucket and rope— her husband the co-conspirator. The treatment was ended forthwith, and obesity continues to stymie doctors to this day.

Life at 150 Mile House was never dull for the dashing young Dr Herald. There were dinners, lively parties, and card-playing evenings. The whole community for miles around joined in dancing that went on until dawn. One Hundred and Fifty Mile House was also the site of the famous "Dead Man's Waltz." A renowned waltz enthusiast died of pneumonia and, at his wake, was whirled around the dance floor for a final gala farewell.

Dr Herald left 150 Mile House in the fall of 1900 after five years of service. He then joined his brother Dundas in a ranching venture near Medicine Hat, Alberta. During the First World War he served overseas as a medical officer with the 72nd Battalion. On returning to the Lower Mainland he practised his specialty for several years. He then moved to Kelowna and, finally, to Nelson. In 1927 he contracted pneumonia while working at a medical clinic in Fernie, BC, and died on New Year's Day at the young age of 57.

In his short life Dr Herald had served his country and his patients honourably and well. In 1901 his replacement at 150 Mile House arrived in the person of Dr Mostyn Hoops, age 49, an 1874 graduate of the famous Rotunda Hospital in Dublin. He was registered as a surgeon and physician in Ireland, and it would seem that he had advanced training in medicine, as he received the MRCP from the Rotunda in 1875. He was registered in BC in 1899.

Laura Moxan recalled that he fit in well in the Cariboo, taking in stride the minus-40-degree-Fahrenheit weather in winter and the dust, mud, and insects in summer. He was to remain for 15 years.

Laura remembers that her mother had an infected bite on her face that swelled and gave her a good deal of pain. A relay of teams and wagons was formed to bring Dr Hoops from 150 Mile House to Alkali, a distance of 20 miles. He brought his wife, son, and daughter with him. "We entertained the young folk and had a great time for several days," said Laura. She mentions that on another occasion her father smashed his finger between two logs while building a fence. She was told to take the team and buggy and go to 150 Mile House to fetch Dr Hoops. This was a 40-mile trip, and, on returning to Alkali Lake, Dr Hoops asked Laura to hold the end of her Dad's finger while he removed a piece of bone. "I was holding it when the doctor looked up and asked how I was doing. I was white as a sheet." "You had better go outside and get some fresh air," he said, "I'll manage."

Irene Stangoe, in *Cariboo Chilcotin*, recounts the occasion when the Ross children of Meldrum Creek had diphtheria. Dr Hoop made the trip across the Fraser River over the New Chimney Creek Bridge and then went on for another 20 miles. He checked the children and advised painting their throats with iodine. All except one survived.

In 1914 he moved to Soda Creek, where a large construction camp was established. The enterprising company of Foley, Welch, and Stewart, upon completing the Grand Trunk Pacific Railway to Prince Rupert, shifted camps south, expecting to build the North South Railway. When this did not materialize the camp was disbanded.

Dr Hoops was not caught short. Now a widower, he married the widow of Peter Dunlevy, one of the early gold seekers in the Cariboo. There is reason to think she entered into this marriage with considerable means. In 1917 Dr Hoops and family moved to Telkwa and, eventually, to the comparative tranquility of general practice at Sydney on Vancouver Island. Then full of memories, he passed away peacefully in his sleep in 1930. The Cariboo remembers him with affection.

It was perhaps no coincidence that another Irish graduate came to 150 Mile House in 1910 to assist Dr Hoops. Cecil Boyd was a 1906

Dr Cecil Boyd, Riske Creek.
Original photo by Carol Hutchison, courtesy of Irene Stangoe.

graduate of Dublin University and also a Rotunda-trained physician. In 1906 he was registered at Bullion Mine near Likely before relocating 50 miles away to the Cariboo Wagon Road community of 150 Mile House. An early picture shows him in a buggy before the two-story Cotton House at Riske Creek, some 30 miles west of his home office. Presumably he was on a house call. A fine-looking team had carried him along at a steady five miles per hour. Molly Forbes tells me that he had a very good reputation. While at 150 Mile House he married a young local woman and, subsequent to this, moved to Victoria—likely in 1918.

Dr Walter Reith Feare replaced Dr Hoops after his move to Soda Creek. He was Canadian-trained, graduating in 1910 from the University of Toronto. His claim to distinction lies in the fact that he delivered Laura Moxan's first two children at home on the Onward Ranch. Dr Feare maintained a large log house near Springhouse as well as one at 150 Mile House and lived at either place, depending on his workload. Springhouse was 15 miles west of 150 Mile House and was connected to it by a narrow winding road. Its position gave better access to calls from the Alkali Lake area as well as to calls from Riske Creek and Meldrum Creek across the Fraser River. The logs from his Springhouse home are still visible. He served until 1918, at which time he moved to Victoria and took up a more settled lifestyle.

Nineteen eighteen marked the beginning of the decline of 150 Mile House. The railway to the north bypassed the community in favour of another small settlement—Williams Lake. After 18 years, 150 Mile House lost its medical doctors.

In 1919 Dr Francis Vere Agnew, a 1912 graduate of Dublin University, arrived via California at Deep Creek, a construction camp 30 miles north of 150 Mile House. Subsequently, in 1920, he moved to Williams Lake. He was the first resident physician at Williams Lake and was soon followed by Dr McKenzie and Dr McRae, thus establishing that community as the new medical centre of the Cariboo.

CHAPTER 20

The Wandering Scot

Dr Wright of Alexis Creek.
Courtesy of Dr John Roberts.

His name was Dr Wright, and his given names were a matter of
some conjecture, but, in the Chilcotin, he was known as Dr William
Wright. An 1876 graduate of the University of Edinburgh, he was a
retired naval officer and ship surgeon, spending much of his life in
the Far East. After leaving the navy in his sixties, he settled at Alexis
Creek in the Chilcotin in central BC. How this came about is simple,
but the factors involved are complex.

Dr William Wright was acquainted with Mrs Norman Lee of
Redstone, probably through contacts in the British Isles. On a visit
to the Lees in 1913, he discovered the Chilcotin. After years in the
confined space of the rolling deck of a ship he was fascinated with
this vast firm land of the Interior plateau. He fell in love with the
open spaces; the horizon; the skies that stretched on forever; and
the independent, laid back pioneers. At age 63 he saw an opportunity
to serve, and for 11 years he was the only doctor for an area covering
15,000 square miles—roughly an area half the size of his native
Scotland. In 1913 he established a practice at Alexis Creek, 80 miles
west of 150 Mile House. For the first year a log cabin provided by the

Grahams served as his lodging and office. Alex Graham provided a loan to erect a hospital and living quarters.

For the following information I am indebted to the Witte sisters; (Veera Bonner, Irene Bliss, and Hazel Litterick), and to June Bliss of Alexis Creek. Frank Witte and Fred Burdett cut and peeled logs; and a local settler, Bob Miller, who was a good axeman, helped to build Dr Wright's hospital. It was finished in 1914, and Dr Wright and his nurse, Miss Goode, moved into its living quarters. The hospital provided surgery and medical attention for serious illnesses. Many babies were delivered here, the first being Bill Graham. Mother and baby were said to have survived the experience in good health.

Dr Wright was 63 years old when he arrived in Alexis Creek. He was described as being a large man with rugged features and a cheerfulness and equanimity that enabled him to surmount the intense cold of the winter as well as the dust and mud of the summer (which, of course, brought with it mosquitoes and insects). He also shared a certain characteristic with people of the Chilcotin: he was oblivious to distance. East of the Fraser River settlers groaned if forced to travel 5 miles to a hay meadow or to move their cattle as much as 10 miles; west of the Fraser River people thought nothing of going 200 miles to the store in Ashcroft, travelling 20 or 30 miles to a hay meadow, or moving their cattle many miles in the middle of winter. It was no coincidence that the longest cattle drive in Canadian history originated in the Chilcotin, with Norman Lee driving cattle 1,500 miles to Teslin in the Yukon. Cattle drives of 160 miles to stockyards in Williams Lake or 200 miles to stockyards in Ashcroft were common. It seemed to come as a matter of course for Dr Wright to travel by buggy six months of the year and by sleigh the other six. It was common for him to travel 30 to 60 miles to call on an ill settler.

Bonnie Church was kind enough to provide me with the handwritten diaries of her father-in-law Herbert Church of Big Creek. In the diaries compiled through the first 30 years of this century there are references to Dr Wright. I note that on November 19, 1913, Dr Wright was paid two dollars for pulling a tooth. At the same time he treated one of the Church girls and also pulled a further two teeth for Mary Church. This may not seem too remarkable, but in November this meant a 30-mile trip by sleigh from Alexis Creek to Big Creek. No doubt he stayed overnight and took his meals with the Churches for at least a day.

In his diary of May 1915 Herbert notes that Dr Wright and his faithful helper, Miss Goode, arrived before supper. They were on their way to visit another patient, but no doubt they were invited to

Alexis Creek Hospital.
(BCARS PDP1641)

spend the night with the Churches. One might conjecture on their sleeping arrangements; that is, whether they were assigned one room or two. The Churches were very straight-laced, and it is likely that the nurse and doctor were given separate rooms. Throughout Dr Wright's years at Alexis Creek there were rumours concerning his relationship with Miss Goode; however, another characteristic of Chilcotin people is that they tend to mind their own business.

In June 1915 there was evidence of a second visit from Dr Wright to Big Creek, and Herbert Church provided transportation for a house call to the Robinsons (six miles from Big Creek), which would be approximately 36 miles from Alexis Creek. The neighbour, Mrs Robinson, was getting along in years and required a good deal of medication and medical care, and on several occasions there are notations that Dr Wright made the 36-mile drive to visit this elderly lady.

On August 15, 1915, Herbert Church's daughter, Dolly, smashed her finger badly and was driven by buggy for an office visit with Dr Wright at Alexis Creek. In February 1916 there was a note that $15 was paid on account for Dr Wright by Herbert Church.

In September 1916 the diaries record that a neighbour, Bob Trethaway, was sick. At that time there were telephones, and Dr Wright was called at Alexis Creek. He arrived by buggy the next day, September 30, only to learn the sad news that Mr Trethaway had passed away the previous day. This was not an uncommon result of serious illnesses in these isolated ranch homes. However, everyone must die at some time, and the best way to die is on one's own ranch, surrounded by loved ones, breathing the clean Chilcotin air with one's last breath, and hearing the bawling of one's own cattle on the hill.

It is noted that in January 1917 Dr Wright called in at the Churches on his way home from the Bambricks. One admires his fortitude, as this required a 33-mile journey by cutter each way. January in the Chilcotin is characterized two-feet-deep snow and minus-40-degree-Fahrenheit temperatures. In November 1919 Dr Wright returned to visit the Churches at Big Creek and stayed overnight; in May 1921 he called in yet again on his way to visit the Robinsons; and in June he made another call on Mrs Robinson, who was quite ill.

In April 1924 Dr Wright called in to examine and treat Percy Church, who was suffering from pleurisy, and in July 1924 Church's diary notes that he had arrived to visit a very sick neighbour by the name of Beck. A further note indicates that the unfortunate Mr Beck died on July 17. This is the last reference in Herbert Church's diary relating to Dr Wright.

June Bliss of Alexis Creek related an episode showing the fortitude of the Natives of the Chilcotin area as well as the skill and medical acumen of Dr Wright. A member of the Anahim reserve, by the name of West, was shot in the lower abdomen. Over the next two days he was brought the 100 miles to Redstone, where Dr Wright met him, having travelled 20 miles from Alexis Creek. After an examination performed in the general store at Redstone, a crude operating theatre was established in an adjoining shed. There Dr Wright, using ether as anaesthetic, opened the wounded Native, corrected the problem, and closed him up. Mr West survived for many years.

A further anecdote is recalled by June Bliss of Alexis Creek and also by the Witte sisters. The Wittes were at Whitewater, some 75 miles from Alexis Creek, with their four children. Two of the girls were eating snowberries without ill effect, but Duane Witte, perhaps eating more than had the others, became very ill from the poison contained in these berries. By wagon he was taken 30 miles over rough, stony, mountainous road, with the parents in the seat and the three little girls huddled in the back. He appeared to be dying. Fifteen hours later they were able to exchange the wagon for a lighter rig and proceeded 27 miles to the settlement of Hanceville. Another 18 miles over somewhat improved roads brought them to the hospital at Alexis Creek, where Dr Wright took over, performing a near miracle in saving the boy's life. It took a number of months for Duane to recover from the effects of the poison.

Irene Stangoe contributed an item culled from the *Williams Lake Tribune* of 1978. It seems that Jimmy Scallon of Big Creek, when his father was very ill, came for Dr Wright with a team and cutter. It was 35 degrees below zero Fahrenheit, and there were three feet of snow. For warmth on the 30-mile journey Dr Wright wore a heavy bearskin coat. In a large inside pocket he had concealed a bottle of brandy, to which he attached a small rubber tube. Every so often he ducked his head inside his coat and had a snort. At the end of the eight hours he was somewhat the worse for wear and had to be given black coffee before he could tend to his patient. Both doctor and patient recovered, both probably benefitting from the contents of the bottle in Dr Wright's coat. Late in 1924 Dr Wright, now 73 years old, could no longer serve the people in the country he loved so much. Leaving Miss Goode to carry on he moved to Vancouver, where, to the sorrow of the people in the Chilcotin, he soon died. The testimony to his life and work is embodied in the affection and respect of the people of the Chilcotin. His failings were few, his virtues many. And his reputation was established by his dedication to his patients as well as by his skill and acumen as a physician and surgeon.

William Wright's official obituary, as carried in Volume 15 of the *Canadian Medical Association Journal* of 1925, adds a note of mystery to this remarkable doctor. Throughout his stay in the Chilcotin he was known as Dr William Wright, yet his registration and obituary gives the name John Henry Wright. It was his son who was named William. No one in the Chilcotin knew that he was married or had children.

Dr John Henry Wright, of Alexis Creek, Chilcotin, BC, died in Vancouver on June 1st, at the age of 73. Dr Wright was a native of Scotland, a graduate of Edinburgh, and came to this province eleven years ago. He leaves a wife and a son, William, to whom our deepest sympathy is extended.

This minor puzzle detracts not one whit from the accomplishments of Dr Wright. May he rest forever in peace.

CHAPTER 21

Dr George Sanson: Medical Giant of Clinton

Dr George Sanson.
(BCARS G-90440)

Dr George Sanson of Ontario exerted almost the same influence on the southern third of central BC as did Doctors Wrinch, Stone, and Baker on the northern half. His life story is one of adventure and service, interspersed with romance, a lovely marriage, and much community involvement.

George Sanson was born in Petrolia, Ontario, circa 1860. While in high school there he fell in love with fellow student Jane MacDonald, and while his advances were not immediately successful, in the end she married him and joined him in his frontier practice.

Sanson proceeded into university and through medical school at the University of Western Ontario, graduating with the degree Medicinae Doctoris Chirurgiae Magister, (MDCM) in 1886. The same year he was registered as the 67th doctor in the College of Physicians and Surgeons of British Columbia. For two years he practised as the company doctor for the Canadian Pacific Railway in Donald in the Canadian Rockies. When construction work was substantially completed, his practice diminished and he moved to Victoria where there were good opportunities for young and skilled men to establish lucrative medical practices. He could not, however, accept the coastal climate, as the constant rainfall seemed to him unhealthy and depressing. Sensibly, he looked about to move to the mainland and was impressed with the climate and terrain of central British Columbia.

From this point on I am indebted to Molly Forbes of Lac La Hache, who is now over 90 years of age. Her parents first lived at Pavilion Mines, then at Clinton. As a young girl, Molly knew Dr Sanson personally. In 1967 and in 1980, respectively, she sent me handwritten accounts of Dr Sanson's activities.

In the late 1800s the Cariboo country was booming with goldmining activities, trading (of both manufactured goods and furs), transportation, government administration, farming, and commerce. The people of the towns of Ashcroft, Lillooet, and Clinton were pressing Victoria to send in a doctor, as, in those days, they could not guarantee enough income to hold one. Few medicines were of any use, and facilities for the performance of surgery were very limited. Skilled medical practitioners were reluctant to waste their talents on these small centres, in spite of the occasional complicated emergency.

The government offered a subsidy as an inducement for trained men to settle in Clinton; 150 Mile House; and, (somewhat later) in the Chilcotin at Alexis Creek. Even with this limited assistance, probably $500 a year, a man needed to be truly dedicated to the profession of medicine to serve such a large and sparsely populated land. To young Dr Sanson, full of enthusiasm and adventure, it was a challenge indeed. His territory stretched from Ashcroft to 100 Mile House and beyond, in one broad sweep taking in Lillooet, Big Bar, Dog Creek, and the lower Chilcotin (in all taking in about 5,000 square miles. Alkali Lake, in the northern Chilcotin, dropped into the bounds of the doctor at 150 Mile House, who served settlements as far north as Quesnel. No rigid boundaries prevailed: whichever doctor was in the best place to provide treatment was the one who answered the call.

Travel was by horse and buggy over roads that were little more than trails. In the winter these trails were snowbound, with

Dr George Sanson (left) and his team of Hamiltonian horses were well known around Clinton. Courtesy of Clinton Museum.

temperatures dropping to 40 degrees Fahrenheit below zero, and in spring and fall they were often high spaces between mud holes. Initially, as Dr Sanson learned the lay of the land, he depended on the Clinton livery station to supply him with transportation; but when his own barn was completed, he purchased a team of Hamiltonians, which served him well for many years. Hamiltonians are intelligent animals, noted for endurance and for maintaining a quick and steady pace of five miles per hour. They could be depended upon to reach isolated ranch houses over unfamiliar roads, often by lantern light. When the moon was high they stepped along as though they knew that time was a factor in their service. The doctor called them Dick and Tommy, and it was with them that he brought his bride to Clinton after their marriage in Petrolia.

Dr Sanson was frequently away from home, making calls either on horseback, in his buggy, or in a cutter. Many injuries, cases of trauma, broken bones, and medical conditions (e.g., pneumonia, digestive upsets, typhoid fever, diphtheria, kidney infections, tumours, and skin conditions) occurred more frequently than they do now. The difference was that then there was very little effective medication available, and surgical amenities were very primitive. Nevertheless, few, if any, calls for help were ignored.

Molly Barton Forbes relates the medical adventures of Alex Meise, later a notable person in the Williams Lake-Horsefly area. Alex, through a misadventure with a rifle, had shattered his right knee and leg bones as well as his femur and tibia. He was presented to Dr Sanson in the old Dominion Hotel in Clinton, and the doctor amputated his leg. Mrs Forbes says that Alex recuperated in her parents' home in Clinton. For many years Alex drove a stagecoach and ran a hotel, with the self-constructed wooden prosthesis being renewed from time to time as circumstances dictated. Throughout his life he showed a touching sense of gratitude to the Barton family for their loving care.

For 16 years Dr Sanson served the Cariboo district. Hundreds of operations were performed in homes, hotel rooms, and tents, as there were no hospitals in which he might exercise his skills. He utilized what few medicines he had, and what surgical facilities were available. And through his ingenuity, flexibility, and skill, he performed medical miracles. On one occasion a local blacksmith formed a crude pair of obstetrical forceps that the doctor used for a complicated delivery.

The Sanson home was perhaps the most luxurious and colourful in Clinton. The garden was graced with flowers, and there were shade trees and a luxurious lawn. An attractive walkway made of tiny, thick slate slabs led from the front gate to the front door. Dr Sanson was to find in his garden and flowering plots a place of relaxation, where most of his frustrations could be resolved into order and beauty.

Dr Sanson and his wife were prominent in city affairs, taking a strong role in education, schools, provincial politics, and the organization of artistic ventures. Many visiting VIPs enjoyed the hospitality of the Sanson home.

In 1912 Dr Sanson felt that opportunities for medical practice were greater in Ashcroft, where the Canadian Pacific Railway provided access, than they were in Clinton. And so he moved his practice to that town, where his life was somewhat easier. A formal office was established, and many patients came to see him there rather than requiring him to make house calls. There was also a small hospital with a recovery room. Emergency care was available through the doctor's nurse, Miss Cadman, and surgical assistants.

Dr Sanson spent his weekends with his wife and two children in Clinton, but in 1910, because of the limited access to educational facilities, Jane Sanson and her son and daughter moved to Victoria. The doctor maintained his residence in Ashcroft, his ties with the Cariboo country being too strong to break.

Dr Sanson was not immune to criticism: a doctor never pleases all the people all the time. Nevertheless, he did what he could. Those requiring more than his rural facilities could provide he sent immediately to specialists in the Lower Mainland—specifically, to

Dr Jones, the famous surgeon in Victoria. Dr Jones was heard to say that Dr Sanson had never made an incorrect diagnosis.

In 1916 Dr Sanson himself was forced to seek the services of Dr Jones. He boarded the CPR train in Ashcroft, refusing to believe that this would be his last trip and his last view of his beloved Cariboo country. During the subsequent operation Dr Jones found advanced cancer, with no possibility of a cure for his colleague and friend. In a moment of exasperation he was heard to say, "Your sense and talents were wasted in that upper country." He changed his mind, however, when he saw the large number of people who came to Victoria to pay him their respects and to carry Dr Sanson to his last resting place back in his beloved Clinton.

Jane survived for another 40 years in Victoria, and at her death was buried beside George in the old-timer's cemetery in Clinton. Son Campbell (a druggist) and daughter Margaret (a school teacher) lived their lives in Victoria. Throughout the years they visited Clinton, the home of their childhood, where two graves and a shell of their former home remained.

The Sanson home in Clinton was finally destroyed by fire, but the true memorial to Dr and Mrs Sanson lies in their work—medical, community, and artistic—which shaped the town of Clinton and the area from Ashcroft to Williams Lake. May they rest in peace on that hillside cemetery in Clinton.

CHAPTER 22

Jane Macdonald Sanson: A Hesitant Bride

The story of George and Jane Sanson has elements of romance and gladness that give their relationship special charm. Both George and Jane were raised in Petrolia, Ontario, which is a town on a Canadian National Railways line, quite distant from any large city. It was during their high-school years that George and Jane became acquainted and developed a friendship that turned into an adolescent romance. Jane, however, was not ready for a serious commitment at the time, and, in spite of George's ardent wooing, temporarily rejected his advances. According to Molly Forbes, who lived in Clinton when Dr. Samson practised there, an exasperated George said, "One day you'll marry me. I will be back to see you. In the meantime you have my heart in your hands. Deal with it carefully."

Following high school George went away to university at Toronto, graduated in medicine, and came west in 1885. In 1887 he moved to Victoria, practised for a short time, and then came to Clinton, BC. It was from Clinton that George again pressed his suit on the affections and heart of Jane MacDonald back in Petrolia. In 1894 a strong-willed Jane yielded and consented not only to marry him, but also to make the long trip from her gentle surroundings in Ontario to the rough frontier community of Clinton.

In the meantime Dr Sanson had purchased land and ordered the building of a fine house, suitable for his new bride. The house was begun in 1894, with logs probably cut on or near the site. A comfortable three-bedroom home was built. To set it apart from the other log buildings of Clinton, Dr Sanson had it completely covered with weatherboard and added a bit of piecrust decoration trim in front. This was to be his bride's first home, and George, with all the enthusiasm and energy of a young lover, made every effort to construct a home worthy of her. The house was built beside a creek that flowed from a little lake on the hills behind. Through natural gravity, cold water was on tap in the house and an ample supply was contained in the lake. And so, in season, the lawn was kept green and the flowers blooming. A picket fence surrounded the landscaped lot, and a barn topped with a good-sized hay mow was also built to stable four horses. A woodshed was built and was painted in colours similar to those of the house: white with red trim.

The newly married young couple came to Ashcroft, where they were met by a buggy drawn by Dr Sanson's spanking team of Hamiltonian horses. A few hours later the new bride was carried over the threshold of her frontier home. Mrs Sanson, although she had come from a more cultured and civilized part of Canada, accepted her role as the wife of a country doctor with fortitude and determination. The doctor had been well aware of these characteristics of Jane's, and perhaps this influenced his ardent pursuit. He needed a wife upon whom he could depend in emergencies and on whom he could lean for moral support in times of extreme stress.

Once settled into their new home, Mrs Sanson took an active part in the affairs of the community. She had the luxury of a maid to care for the household work and so had more time than did the average woman to devote to activities outside her home. She played the organ in the Presbyterian Church and, with her help, a timid choir was soon singing hosannas that must have been heard in heaven. Her influence in the school was very strong. First-year teachers often found encouragement and ready help, particularly if their methods and ideas were congenial to those of Mrs Sanson, who favoured discipline and attention to the three R's.

Many famous guests were hosted in the Sanson house, and the Clinton school children could always count on a big summer party on the lawn. Best of all, Mrs Sanson's sister, Trixie Campbell of Victoria, was a very talented singer and, on yearly trips to Clinton, presented musical concerts. Molly Forbes says that Mrs Campbell's grandson was none other than Ian Tyson of Ian and Sylvia fame.

The Sansons' idyllic lifestyle continued for almost 15 years. Dr Sanson often looked to the home as a fortress where he could find peace and relaxation. Riches were not a part of a frontier doctor's expectations. In fact, it was often difficult for them to make a decent living. As has been mentioned, in 1910 Dr Sanson moved to Ashcroft in the hope that it would offer him a busier practice. Mrs Sanson carried on in Clinton; son Campbell took full charge of the saddle horses, dogs, and other animals left in Clinton; and daughter Margaret finished grade school. Once Margaret had completed school, Jane and her two children moved to Victoria, while George commuted back and forth from Ashcroft. George died of cancer in 1916, and Jane lived on for another 40 years. On her death she was buried beside him in Clinton (see Chapter 25).

CHAPTER 23

Doctor Dundas Herald
The Doctor by the Gold Rush Trail

Dundas Herald (2nd from right, back row), 1890, Anatomy class.
Courtesy of Archives, Queens University, Kingston, ON.

Dundas Herald was content to abide by the trail at Quesnelle Forks in central BC. He did not join the adventurous miners who pushed on to Barkerville, Manson Creek, and the Klondike. The small village of Quesnelle Forks, nestled between the north and south branches of the Quesnelle River, attracted him, and, in 1896, this is where he established his practice. Later, he was to serve the nearby settlements of Likely and Bullion Mine.

At the turn of the century Quesnelle Forks was reached by taking the stagecoach from Ashcroft to 150 Mile House (a jarring three-day journey), then by taking the connecting coach to Harper's Camp at Horsefly, and, finally, by taking a coach or riding a horse for the next 50 miles north (a two-day journey). In the 1890s Quesnelle Forks was in decline, following the exhaustion of gold-bearing river deposits (rich gold strikes dated back to 1859). There were 200 people in the community, mostly miners and Chinese labourers. Several saloons were in operation, and the Tong House provided a social and gambling centre for the Chinese. Opium was legal and was widely used by the Chinese.

In 1897 an active community was founded south of Likely, which was 12 miles south of Quesnelle Forks. Here the Cariboo Hydraulic Company employed 150 men. There was a store, a sawmill, and a small hospital.

Dr Dundas Herald, born in 1870 in Dundas, Ontario, was the son of a Presbyterian clergyman, the Reverend James Herald. He was the third member of his family to attend Queen's University, graduating from its medical college in 1891. He set out for British Columbia immediately upon graduation and was registered by that province's college of physicians and surgeons in 1891, a few months after his brother Wilson was registered.

Both brothers practised in Vancouver for the next four years and then moved north—Wilson to Ashcroft and 150 Mile House, Dundas

Quesnelle Forks, c. 1880.
(BCARS A-04045)

to Quesnelle Forks. Apparently asthma, worsened by Vancouver's rain, was a factor in Dundas's move. Neither doctor had a wife or family with him, and it may be assumed that Dundas frequently visited 150 Mile House to partake of its lively social life.

While Wilson obtained a government grant to practise in the Cariboo, there is no record in the BC accounts that Dundas applied for this $500 yearly incentive. Dr Wilkins, who followed him, did receive this grant. Interestingly enough, there is little information available regarding Dr Herald's five-year medical practice in Quesnelle Forks. An 1899 a notation in the *Bullion Mine Journal* mentions that, after a night spent delivering twins to a Mrs McRae of Quesnelle Forks, Dundas arrived at 6:00 AM at the mine to pronounce dead a Mr Rodini. This sort of a night guaranteed grey hair for any practitioner.

The miners had ready access to the best analgesic available (then and now) in the form of opium and morphine. And while ether and chloroform were also available, it is unlikely that much surgery was performed in this isolated area. The doctor had little in his armamentarium to alter the course of severe illnesses, and he was probably not routinely consulted.

There is little evidence that Dr Herald practised medicine after he left Quesnelle Forks in 1901, although he remained on the register of the College of Physicians and Surgeons of British Columbia until 1918. He did establish a cattle ranch with brother Wilson at Medicine Hat, Alberta. Then, in 1906, after marrying Edith Walsh of Corona, Ontario, he moved to Salmon Arm where Sunny Brae Farm was established from virgin forest land on Shuswap Lake.

Dundas Herald died in 1951 at the age of 80, a well respected settler of the Okanagan. Today his name is commemorated in Herald Park, on the Sunny Brae site, which was purchased by the provincial government from his daughter Jessie Herald in 1975.

The mural in the lobby of G.R. Baker Memorial Hospital Quesnel captures the essence of pioneer doctoring. Courtesy of Marjorie Lee.

CHAPTER 24

Medical And Surgical Emergencies In Pioneer Times

Pioneer doctors dealt with every infirmity and calamity that can befall the human body. With few effective medicines available surgeons often practised in primitive surroundings. Still, even though the natural recuperative powers of the human body were usually diminished by poor diet and physical hardship, doctors were often successful in their efforts. When medical skills were unequal to the task, there was always the graveyard.

The inhabitants of central BC were generous in their praise of and appreciation for medical people, and they tended to be accepting when the fortunes of their beloved or friends and acquaintances were less than happy. A tour through the Barkerville cemetery is an eye-opener for those of us who are used to the effectiveness of modern medicine. There are so many babies laid to rest, so many accident victims, so many lost through pneumonia. And everywhere one sees the graves of young men 20 to 30 years of age. Surrounded by trees is the grave of at least one of the medical doctors who dealt with the health problems of the community—Dr Thomas Bell.

Barkerville was comparatively well off compared to Ankitlas, where Dr Robert Tomlinson served. In Ankitlas the ordinary run of diseases was complicated by frostbite and malnutrition. Mrs Tomlinson nearly died from typhoid fever and hunger, and Robert nearly froze to death in making a house call to attend a gunshot wound at the village of Kispiox (see Chapter 3).

Jessie Gould of Hazelton records Dr Wrinch's management of the victim of a grizzly bear mauling circa 1913. The story shows the traditional stoicism of a Native who, when out hunting, was beset by a grizzly bear, mauled, and left for dead. The grizzly bear was mistaken however, and the poor victim revived and managed to cover the two miles to the nearest cabin. There his terrible wounds were tied up somehow, and he started for a hospital 30 miles away. The nurse who received him told in amazement how he arrived sitting upright in a cart with his bandaged head erect, singing his death song. Eight months later he was discharged from the hospital.

Accidents related to farming, logging, construction, and mining were a frequent challenge to the early doctors. In 1960 Angus Nikal, a Native, presented himself at the Wrinch Memorial Hospital with a chronic granulating wound over his lower leg. Apparently he had fractured it in 1912 while working for the Grand Trunk Pacific Railway and had been cared for by Dr Wrinch. Over the years this chronic wound developed. On probing the wound, it was obvious that there was a steel plate still in place from the setting of the leg fracture in 1912. When this plate was removed the wound healed.

Dr Baker of Quesnel had his own method of dealing with haematomas of the brain occasioned by mine accidents. He drilled bore holes through the skull and, with a sharp blow from his hand, evacuated the collected blood.

The Spanish flu epidemic of 1919 was a terrible scourge and stressed the attending doctors to the limit. Friends and neighbours in all communities died like flies. Dr Wrinch of Hazelton travelled from home to home by day and night and was often found sleeping in his wagon or sleigh by the side of the road, completely exhausted. Dr Baker of Quesnel had his own treatment, which consisted of a giant mustard plaster extending from hips to neck, together with two different pills of unknown nature. Long before ideas concerning the healing touch, his constant attention brought the Quesnel area through the flu epidemic with a limited number of fatalities.

In Prince George the epidemic struck almost every household. I am fortunate to have an account written by David T. Williams, an old-timer in the area, which provides a picture of the epidemic from a patient's standpoint.

> *Some time in the late fall of 1918 the Spanish influenza came to Prince George. I can recall schools closing, in addition to which the original Connaught School, which I attended, was used as a hospital. We would find all manner of things, including bed pans, in the cupboards when we returned.*
>
> *I was the first to take sick at home. When I was nearly recovered, the next one took sick. As a family we were fortunate that while all the ten children were sick at times, we all recovered, as did our parents.*
>
> *Through it all we sold milk to the Isowski household. I can remember Nestor Isowski and I meeting at a midpoint. We never got within 100 feet*

of each other. He set down a scalded, steaming pot, then retreated. I advanced, poured the milk out from my container, then left, while he advanced to take up his and went home. There, I have no doubt, the milk was boiled.

Doctors in those days had a habit of setting bright, glaring placards on homes with any kind of infectious disease; "Quarantined" for 40 days. There were no placards at home for the flu. Perhaps it was too widespread.

Many years later, when I was in charge of Prince George City Hall, I talked to Mr Harry Perry, who told me of his experiences as mayor during this time:

I was 26 years old and had to organize the city. Foot patrols were sent out to every home every day to do the necessary things. I called a meeting of all the doctors and the city council. We asked them what the cure and treatment was. They said they did not know much about it. The usual supportive measures helped, as for the medicine they thought that quinine and whisky might be of use, but there was prohibition in the land. So I took the chief of police and his biggest constable and went to all the hotels likely to have whisky. Of course they protested they had none.

I told them we would tear down the premises board by board and throw them onto the street until we found the whisky, as there were men, women, and children dying every day. We got the whiskey. Official notices were put in the paper. No public meetings or even church services were allowed. Patrols had to report every case to Dr Lyon. With good care deaths were low, but poor care and conditions made the disease lethal. The Union Hotel and the Connaught were pressed into service as hospitals. The sawmill camps east of town were very hard hit. George Williams and J.A. Davis organized South Fort George. Wood and water were made available. Morice Quah saw to it that no Indian died without proper burial and a record of death. They were supplied with liquor by cooperating with local provincial officials. Nevertheless, 10 percent of the 1400 local Indians died, also 42 in Stoney Creek near Vanderhoof.

R.F. Corless was the local undertaker. This man was very versatile and ingenious, and a former contractor for the city. I imagine he had a good supply of liquor to help him out. The [following] story was told of his resourcefulness. Three bodies were starting to smell, [and they] could not be buried until they were identified. Dick [Corless] came into the room. "Why," says he, "this one is Olef Olefson. I knew him well. Here is poor old Quan Lee, and we'll bury Pocahontas with her people."

This same flu extended to a large area of the world. Claim was made of 6 million dead in 12 weeks. Vital statistics in Victoria have a record of a death rate for that year of 15 per thousand, compared to a usual 10 per thousand. This was for white people. In Vancouver you had to have a face mask before boarding a street car. In Prince George the flu faded out by year's end. We went back to Connaught School. My brother said his room was the acute care room and 42 people had died there.

So passed the great flu epidemic. One doctor was thought to have perished, but, surprisingly, most of them carried on and attended to their patients through the entire epidemic. There is little wonder that, faced with the possibility of a similar epidemic a few years ago, the whole of Canada was galvanized into implementing the requisite protective measures.

CHAPTER 25

Pioneer Doctors:
An Everlasting Monument

On looking back on the medical pioneers of central British Columbia, it comes as a shock to realize that all of them are dead—their remains interred in scattered graves in the vast central Interior. Ashes to ashes, dust to dust: their bodies have rejoined the earth from which they were created. However, their true images are not in these rude clods but in the memories that live in the children and grandchildren of the people that they served so well. These people remember the terrible responsibilities carried, the physical hardships endured, and the years of service given by the pioneer doctors.

How many physicians nowadays will set forth on a saddle horse for a 30-mile ride through a blizzard and minus-30-degree-Fahrenheit temperatures to offer medical care to a sick individual? Particularly given that, at the time, the medical armamentarium was so limited that the main factors in successful treatment were the patient's own bodily defences and the art of medicine. These physicians were completely committed to their patients, and the latter had immense respect and affection for the former. Next to God, people loved and trusted their doctor.

Some pioneer doctors had characters that bore the mark of greatness. They were both mentally and physically tough. Dr Tomlinson came from Ireland to bring his medical skills to the isolated tribes along the Northwest Coast of BC, and for 45 years he faced the violence of ocean storms and winter cold to go from one isolated village to another. Dr Wrinch paddled 200 miles up the raging Skeena River with his new bride to establish a medical mission at the isolated Native village of Kispiox. The Barkerville doctors came from Britain, Ireland, and Eastern Canada, and they lived and died in the brawling, vibrant frontier gold town of Barkerville.

Dr Baker, after attaining postgraduate training in the heart of London, immigrated to North America and practised medicine in the wild frontier, even riding shotgun for shipments of gold for Wells Fargo. Dr Sanson of Clinton thought nothing of undertaking 50-mile trips by buggy behind his Hamiltonian horses to bring medical attention to an isolated farmer or trapper in the Clinton-100 Mile

House area. Their endurance and courage was only surpassed by that of their wives, five of whom died before reaching the age of 55.

A further characteristic of these doctors was their intrepid approach to the hardships of the frontier. Distance, weather, road conditions—nothing deterred them. Dr Wrinch snowshoed 120 miles so he would not be late in taking his registration examinations at the College of Physicians and Surgeons of British Columbia. Dr Tomlinson snowshoed seven miles at 60 degrees Fahrenheit below zero to attend a patient and then nearly froze to death in an unheated cabin. He was sustained only by the warmth of a pack of mongrel dogs that clung to him. Dr Stone travelled 70 miles each way in early winter to fulfil his duties as coroner on a murder case, and Dr Baker of Quesnel travelled all over the Quesnel-Chilcotin area to look after patients, often performing operations in isolated cabins or tents.

One characteristic that made these doctors so beloved was that they shared the fortune and hardships of the people to whom they ministered. Not one of them died rich, in spite of years of service. Dr Cuzner, in 40 years of practice, did not send out one bill; he relied on people's generosity and ability to pay. Dr Baker died with very little, and the reason (given by people who knew him) is that he gave away so much of what he received. The doctors of Barkerville were scarcely able to make ends meet with the money they received, yet, in spite of this, they persisted through the years. Dr Sanson of Clinton received only a pittance to sustain his family and was forced to move his practice to Ashcroft to make an adequate living. He refused to move his practice to a more lucrative area in a larger city.

People, seeing the sacrifices made by their doctors, realized their generosity and repaid them with respect and love. These pioneer doctors, for the most part, literally burned themselves out in the service of their patients. The challenges that they left to the doctors of today are: dare the elements; give your bodies and health in the service of others; maintain and advance your skills as physicians; and, above all, make the welfare of your patients your foremost concern. For the pioneer doctors, wealth, leisure, and pleasure were always secondary to devotion to profession and responsibility to patients. May we in the noble profession of medicine hold high these pioneer doctors and be faithful to the example they have set for us.

Harp of the North, farewell! The hills grow dark,
On purple peaks a deeper shade descending;
In twilight copse the glow-worm lights her spark,
The deer, half-seen, are to the covert wending.

And now, 'tis silent all!—Enchantress, fare thee well!

Walter Scott, *Lady of the Lake*

Pioneers—farewell.

Sources

Chapter 1

Hieber, Paul; Mayfield, Patricia; Willms, John. Personal communication.

Harmon, Daniel William. 1922. *A Journal of Voyages and Travel in the Interior of North America*. New York: AMS Press.

Morice, Father A.G. 1973. *The History of the Northern Interior of British Columbia*. Smithers: Interior Stationer.

Chapter 2

Cariboo Sentinel, 1863-67. British Columbia Archives and Records Service, Victoria.

College of Physicians and Surgeons of British Columbia Library. Vancouver, Medical Registers, 1890-1924.

Daily British Colonist (Victoria). 1913. 23 May, p. 10

Elliott, Gordon P. 1968. *Barkerville, Quesnel and the Cariboo Gold Rush*. Vancouver: Douglas and McIntyre.

Chapter 3

Large, R.G. 1968. *Drums and Scalpel*. Vancouver: Mitchell Press.

____. 1996. *Skeena: River of Destiny,* 6th ed. Surrey: Heritage House.

Tomlinson, Robert Jr. 1955. Journal and letters.

Chapter 4

Gould, Jessie. Personal communication.

Large, R.G. 1968. *Drums and Scalpel*. Vancouver: Mitchell Press.

____. 1996. *Skeena: River of Destiny,* 6th ed. Vancouver: Heritage.

Tomlinson, Robert Jr. 1953. Journal and letters.chapter five

Chapter 5

Gould, Jessie. Personal communication, handwritten journal.

Lee, Eldon. 1957-59. Personal notes taken as resident doctor at Hazelton Hospital.

United Church of Canada. 1929. Board of Home Missions, Hospital Committee Report, 5 February.

Wrinch, H.G. 1921. *Hazelton Hospital, Annual Report*.

Chapter 6

Gould, Jessie. Personal communication, journals, and pictures.

Hazelton Hospital. 1906-34. Annual Reports.

Chapter 7

Baker, G.R. to Fred Lindsay. 1946. Quesnel Museum.

British Columbia. 1897. College of Physicians and Surgeons. Medical Register.

Fraser, Gertrude; Holley, Al; LeBourdais, Maude. Personal communication.

____. 1995. College of Physicians and Surgeons. Medical Library.

Douglas, Gilean. 1968. "Doctor for the Cariboo." *Daily Colonist* (Victoria), 17 April, p. 7.

Holley, Alex. Personal communication.

Le Bourdais, Louis. 1930. "Dr Baker Went to Cariboo to Stay One Night." *Vancouver Province*, 6 September.

Quesnel Advertiser. 1955. "The Cariboo Doctor." 26 November, p. 9.

____. 1955. "The Hospital Story." 26 November, p. 3.

Chapter 8

Douglas, Gilean. 1975. "Cariboo Doctor." *Daily Colonist* (Victoria), 11 September.

Fraser, John. 1958. "A Tribute." *Quesnel Advertiser*, 26 November.

Fraser, Gertrude Watt. Personal communication.

Holley, Alex. Personal communication.

LeBourdais, Louis. 1930. "Dr Baker Went to The Cariboo to Stay One Night." *Vancouver Province*, 6 April.

LeBourdais, Maude. Personal communication.

Chapter 9

Cronin, Kay. 1960. *A Cross in the Wilderness*. Vancouver: Mitchell.

Foote, Grace. 1986. *Deeper Roots and Greener Valleys*. Fraser Lake BC: Fraser Lake and District Historical Society.

Hancock, Lyn. 1979. *Vanderhoof; The Town that Wouldn't Wait*. Vanderhoof: Nechako Valley Historical Society.

Runnalls, F.E. 1946. *History of Prince George*. Vancouver: Wrigley Printers.

Trick, Bernice. 1986. "From a Missionary to State of the Art." *Prince George Citizen*, 26 July, p. 5.

Chapter 10

British Columbia. 1900, 1916, 1924. College of Physicians and Surgeons. Medical Register.

Foote, Grace. 1986 *Deeper Roots and Greener Valleys*. Fraser: Lake, BC: Fraser Lake and District Historical Society.

____. Personal communication.

McKenna, Jean. Personal communication.

Mummery, Marion. Personal communication.

Foote, Grace; Fraser Lake and District Historical Society; Fraser Lake, BC, 1986.

Library, College of Physicians and Surgeons of British Columbia, Medical Register, 1900, 1916, 1924.

Chapter 11

Foote, Grace. 1986. *Deeper Roots and Greener Valleys*. Fraser Lake, BC: Fraser Lake and District Historical Society.

____. Personal communication.

Hendrie, Millie. Personal communication.

McKenna, Jean. Personal communication.

Philpott, Vesta. Personal communication.

Chapter 12

Foote, George. Personal communication.

Foote, Grace. 1986. *Deeper Roots and Greener Valleys*. Fraser Lake, BC: Fraser Lake and District Historical Society

Hancock, Lyn. 1979. *Vanderhoof: The Town that Wouldn't Wait*. Vanderhoof: Nechako Valley Historical Society.

Hendrie, Millie. Personal communication.

McDonnell, Ed. Personal communication.

McIntosh, Lil. Personal communication.

Chapter 13

British Columbia. 1893-1924. College of Physicians and Surgeons. Medical Registers.

Hazelton Hospital. 1921. Annual Report.

Rudland, Lenore. 1988. *Fort Fraser (Where the Hell Is That?)*. Fort Fraser, BC: E. and L. Rudland.

Turkki, Pat. 1973. Burns Lake and District. Burns Lake, BC: Burns Lake and District Historical Society.

Williams, Ted. Personal communication

Chapter 14

Calvert, Margaret. Personal communication.

Hancock, Lyn. 1979. *Vanderhoof: The Town that Wouldn't Wait.* Vanderhoof: Nechako Valley Historical Society.

McIntosh, Lil. Personal communication.

Chapter 15

Calvert, Margaret. Personal communication.

Chapter 16

Ewert, Robert. Personal communication.

Ford, Isabel. Personal communication.

Kaufman, Edmund. 1972. *General Conference Mennonite Pioneers.* North Newton, KA: Bethel College.

Kerr, The Rev. Personal communication.

O'Sullivan, Evelyn. 1989. *Street Names of Prince George: Our History,* Prince George: College of New Caledonia Press.

Prince George Citizen, Various issues.

Sinclair, Elizabeth. Personal communication

Chapter 17

Boehler, Gladys. Personal communication.

British Columbia. 1916. College of Physicians and Surgeons. Medical Register.

Cadden, Catherine. Personal communication.

Ford, Isabel. Personal communication.

Prince George Citizen. 1949. Various issues.

Chapter 18

McKenna, Jean. Personal communication.

Keefe, Alice. Personal communication.

Mummery, Marion. Personal communication.

Chapter 19

British Columbia. 1896-1924. College of Physicians and Suregons. Medical Register.

British Columbia Public Accounts. 1894-1901. Parliament Buildings, Victoria.

Forbes, Molly. Personal communication.

Moxan, Laura. Personal communication.

Queen's University Archives. 1889-91. Alumni files.

Roberts, Dr John. Personal communication.

Stangoe, Irene. 1994. *Cariboo-Chicotin, Pioneer People and Places*. Surrey: Heritage House.

____. Personal communication.

Vancouver Sun. 1927. "Obituaries." 30 April, p. 8

Chapter 20

Bliss, June. Personal communication.

Bonner, Veera. Personal communication.

Bonner, Vera, Irene Bliss, and Hazel Letterick. 1995. *Chilcotin: Preserving Pioneer Memories*. Surrey: Heritage.

Church, Herman. 1912-24. Diaries (supplied by Bonnie Church).

Roberts, Dr John. Personal communication.

Stangoe, Irene. Personal communication.

Telford, Kathleen. Personal communication.

Williams Lake Tribune. 1978. "Chilcotin Doctor".

Chapter 21

British Columbia. 1893. College of Physicians and Surgeons of British Columbia, Medical Register.

Forbes, Molly. 1967. Journals and letters.

Chapter 22

Forbes, Molly. Personal communication.

Chapter 23

British Columbia. 1896-1918. College of Physicians and Surgeons of British Columbia. Medical Registers.

Hedon, Pat. Personal communication.

Queen's University Archives. 1885-91. Alumni.

Chapter 24

Perry, Harry. Personal communication.

Williams, David. Personal papers.

Index

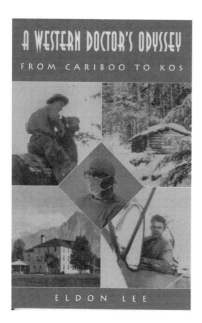

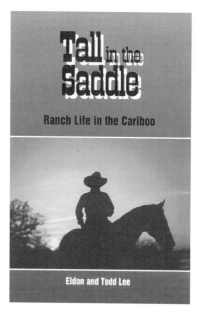

A Western Doctor's Odyssey
From Cariboo to Kos

Dr. Eldon Lee

Raised on a Cariboo ranch, Eldon Lee turned to a medical career after RCAF duty in WW II. Medical training in Seattle and Vancouver precluded his return to central BC as a young practitioner in Hazelton, BC. In this setting Dr. Lee explores the values and events that instilled in him a life long commitment to the Hippocratic oath *to keep the welfare of patients always foremost.*

ISBN 1-895811-21-X
Softcover • $11.95

Tall in the Saddle
Ranch Life in the Cariboo

Eldon and Todd Lee

An isolated Cariboo ranch with sub-zero winters was a startling contrast to California but for the Lee boys it promised huge adventure. Between them they had only one year of formal education but a dedicated mother and home learnin' seemed to work. Dr Eldon Lee delivered 4,000 babies and Reverend Todd wrote a host of books.

ISBN 1-895811-44-9
Softcover • $14.95

Pioneer Voices

A Word About the Heritage House
Pioneer Voices Series

Cariboo-Chicotin: Pioneer People and Places. Irene Stangoe's first book was picked by *BC Bookworld* as one of the province's all-time favorites. Now in its second printing, 28 tales of the past entertain and inform the reader in a folksy style spiced with humour and insight. ($12.95)

Looking Back at the Cariboo-Chilcotin with Irene Stangoe made its way onto best sellers lists with more great yarns about central BC pioneers. ($14.95)

Totem Poles and Tea by Hughina Harold has been called "an adult version of *Anne of Green Gables*" and a "must-read for all BCers" by independent reviewers. It is an enlightening story of a young nurse-teacher's coming of age in a remote 1930s native village. ($17.95)

Tales of a Pioneer Journalist by David W. Higgins brings alive 19th century life during the BC gold rush and formative years of Victoria. Higgins, one of the era's most colourful journalists and former Speaker of the BC Legislature, entertains and informs his readers with a style deemed by one reviewer as "un-put-downable." ($16.95)

Cariboo Cowboy by Harry Marriott, written in the 1950s, remains the best of campfire reading for horse and nature lovers throughout the west. The ranch setting of Big Bar Lake captures the soul of cowboy life and the dignity of Harry and Peg Marriott. ($14.95)

More Books on the Cariboo-Chilcotin

Goldpanning in the Cariboo by Charles Hart and Jim Lewis. The first in the Creeks of Gold Series. A detailed guide book designed to help everybody enjoy the beauty of BC's back country while exploring proven gold-bearing creeks long associated with one of the world's great gold rushes. ($9.95)

Trails to Gold, Volume II by Branwen Patenaude. The pioneer roadhouses between Clinton and Barkerville provide us a living heritage of the colourful era of the Cariboo Gold Rush. The trail was ever changing and when the rush was over, the Cariboo-Chilcotin was left with a mosaic of roadhouses and a legacy to build on. ($18.95)

Chilcotin: Preserving Pioneer Memories by the Witte sisters. A vivid text and over 200 photographs recall country extending some 200 miles west from the Fraser River to Anahim Lake. ($39.95)

Cariboo Gold Rush. The saga of 30,000 chasing one of the world's richest discoveries in 1858. They found nuggets by the ton and carved a web of trails and memories into the heart of BC. Maps, photos, bar room tales, success, tragedy and characters galore. ($7.95)

Wagon Road North by Art Downs. One of BC's most popular books with sales over 130,000. Compiled from diaries, journals, eye-witness reports and similar sources. Over 200 photos (16 pages in full color) including St. Saviour's Church, now over 100 years old, and the nearby 1863 graveyard. ($16.95)

About the Author

Born in Chico, California in 1923, Eldon Lee was raised with his younger brother, Todd, on a Cariboo ranch before entering military service to become an RCAF bomber pilot. Eldon graduated from the University of Washington Medical School in 1952. He spent his internship and residency years at Vancouver General and Shaughnessy hospitals in Vancouver, British Columbia.

After completing his medical training, Eldon embarked on his first stint as a rural doctor. With wife Marjorie and their first of six children, the young doctor accepted a position near what was still a frontier of modern life, Hazelton, BC.

Subsequent to his years in Hazelton, Eldon specialized in obstetrics at Vancouver General, then spent a year as Registrar at Marston Green Maternity Hospital in England. On his return to North America, for many years he practised as the only obstetrician and gynaecologist in the vast reaches of central BC, north of the fifty-first parallel. Here, he and Marjorie raised six children.

Resident in the community of Prince George for three decades, Eldon Lee is a life member of various medical colleges, associations and societies. He devotes his retirement years to recreational flying, the study of post-graduate Greek, teaching Sunday School and his interest in both fiction and non-fiction writing.

Dr Lee recently celebrated his forty-fifth wedding anniversary with Marjorie and has always recognized the major role she has played in his successful professional life.

In 1995, Eldon co-authored *Tall in the Saddle* with his later brother, Todd. He followed that with an account of his years in Hazelton, *A Western Doctor's Odyssey, From Cariboo to Kos*. Eldon is now working on his fourth book for Heritage.